Flood Estimation Handbook

Books are to be returned on or before
the last date below.

Volume 1

**7–DAY
LOAN**

2 3 APR 2004

2 4 SEP 2004

1 4 FEB 2005

LIBREX —

Flood Estimation Handbook

Volume 1
Overview

Duncan Reed

Institute of Hydrology

© **Institute of Hydrology 1999**

ISBN for complete set of 5 volumes: 0 948540 94 X
ISBN for this volume: 0 948540 89 3

Institute of Hydrology
Crowmarsh Gifford
Wallingford
Oxfordshire
OX10 8BB
UK

Tel: 01491 838800
Fax: 01491 692424
http://www.nwl.ac.uk/ih

Cover photo: Evesham Journal

Cross-referencing

Cross-references to other parts of the Handbook are usually abbreviated. They are indicated by the relevant volume number preceding the chapter, section or sub-section number, with the volume number in bold (e.g. **5** 7.2 refers to Section 7.2 of Volume 5). Cross-references conventionally prefixed by Chapter, Section or § are to the current volume (e.g. §2.5 refers to the section Duty of care).

Contents

Preface   ix

Notation   xi

Chapter 1   Introduction   1
       1.1   Foreword   1
       1.2   How the Handbook came about   1
       1.3   What the Handbook intends   2
       1.4   Structure of Handbook   2
       1.5   Only a guidebook   4
       1.6   Structure of Volume 1   4

Chapter 2   Using the Handbook   5
       2.1   Approaches to flood frequency estimation   5
       2.2   Maxims for flood frequency estimation   5
       2.3   Data transfers   6
       2.4   Summary of resources   6
       2.5   Duty of care   9
       2.6   Digital catchment data   9
       2.7   Learning from mistakes   10
       2.8   Revision policy   10

Chapter 3   Using the Handbook procedures   11
       3.1   Scope   11
       3.2   Basic concepts   12
       3.3   Selecting donor and analogue catchments   13

Chapter 4   Principal new features   15

Chapter 5   Which method to use   17
       5.1   Introduction   17
       5.2   Preliminary considerations   17
       5.3   Choice of method within the statistical approach   18
       5.4   Choice of method within the rainfall-runoff approach   19
       5.5   Factors influencing the choice between statistical and
             rainfall-runoff approaches   20
       5.6   Reconciling estimates from the statistical and
             rainfall-runoff approaches   21
       5.7   Choice of method when the catchment is urbanised   21
       5.8   Additional possibilities   23

Chapter 6   Finding data   24
       6.1   Extreme rainfall data   24
       6.2   Flood peak data   24
       6.3   Flood event data   25
       6.4   Historical flood data   25

Interlude   A sideways look at UK flood frequency estimation   27

Overview

Chapter 7   Climate change   38
    7.1 Background   38
    7.2 Climate change impact assessment   40
    7.3 Detecting climate change impacts   42

Chapter 8   Development-control applications   44
    8.1 Introduction   44
    8.2 Judging the extent of catchment urbanisation   44
    8.3 Discussion of methods   45

Chapter 9   Flood risk mapping   47
    9.1 Requirement   47
    9.2 Indicative maps of flood risk and floodplain extent   47
    9.3 A flood risk myth   48
    9.4 A workable approach   49
    9.5 Automated flood risk mapping   49
    9.6 Whole catchment modelling   50

Chapter 10 Flood frequency estimation for public safety   51
    10.1 Impounding reservoirs   51
    10.2 Other sensitive sites   53
    10.3 Short-term forecasting of flood risk   53
    10.4 New approaches to reservoir flood estimation   53

Chapter 11 Checklists   55

Chapter 12 Looking ahead   56
    12.1 Statistical flood frequency estimation   56
    12.2 Rainfall-runoff methods   57
    12.3 The digital revolution   58
    12.4 Catchment description   60
    12.5 Trend detection   60
    12.6 Flood runoff effects of development   61
    12.7 Closure   61

Acknowledgements   62

References   63

Appendix A Return period, risk and resampling   67
    A.1 Return period   67
    A.2 Risk equation   67
    A.3 Resampling methods   68

Appendix B Joint probability problems   74
    B.1 Some examples   74
    B.2 Dice problems   75
    B.3 How flooding problems differ from dice problems   77
    B.4 Summary of the double matrix method   82
    B.5 Avoiding joint probability problems   86
    B.6 Further guidance   87

Contents

Appendix C   Augmenting flood estimates by historical review   89
   C.1   Why carry out a historical review?   89
   C.2   Sources of historical information   90
   C.3   Interpretation   91

Appendix D   Bibliography of related technical guidance   95
   D.1   Introduction   95
   D.2   Series and institutions   95
   D.3   Other publications   98

Index   102

Preface

The research for the Flood Estimation Handbook was undertaken at the Institute of Hydrology, Wallingford, Oxfordshire. The Institute is an integral part of the Centre for Ecology and Hydrology, and a component institute of the Natural Environment Research Council. The research programme ran from 1994 to 1999.

Contributors

The core research team comprised Duncan Reed (team leader), Adrian Bayliss, Duncan Faulkner, Helen Houghton-Carr, Dörte Jakob, David Marshall, Alice Robson and Lisa Stewart. David Jones acted as an internal consultant, advising on all aspects of the research. The WINFAP-FEH software package was principally developed by Lawrence Beran, and the FEH CD-ROM was designed and developed by Kevin Black. The Handbook is dedicated in memory of Tanya Jones, a team member whose contribution to hydrological research was tragically cut short by cancer.

Major contributions were also made by David Morris, Susan Morris, Christel Prudhomme and Robert Scarrott, with additional contributions by Val Bronsdon, Victoria Edmunds, Beate Gannon, Stephanie Hills and Nick Reynard.

The team was supported by 1-year Sandwich Course Students from Luton and Sheffield Hallam Universities, including: Mark Bennett, Robert Brookes, Russell Brown, Louisa Coles, Nick Davie, Philip Davies, David Hewertson, Catriona Kelly, Marina Syed Mansor and Paul Nihell.

Sponsors

The research programme was funded by the Ministry of Agriculture Fisheries and Food (MAFF), the Environment Agency, the Department of Agriculture Northern Ireland, and a consortium led by the Scottish Office. The budget for the programme totalled about £1.7m. Indirect support was provided by the Centre for Ecology and Hydrology, the Meteorological Office, and river gauging authorities. Costs of final editing and publication of the Handbook, and development of the WINFAP-FEH software, were met by the Institute of Hydrology.

Advisers

The research was reviewed by the Flood Estimation Handbook Advisory Group, comprising:

David Richardson, MAFF Flood and Coastal Defence *(Chair)*
Linda Aucott, Environment Agency
Alan Burdekin, Scottish Office
John Clarke, Department of Agriculture, Northern Ireland
Christopher Collier, University of Salford
Conleth Cunnane, University College Galway, Ireland
John Goudie, MAFF Flood and Coastal Defence *(Technical Secretary)*
Richard Harpin, Sir William Halcrow and Partners
David MacDonald, Binnie Black and Veatch
Andrew Pepper, Consultant to the Environment Agency *(Observer)*
Duncan Reed, Institute of Hydrology
Richard Tabony, Meteorological Office
Howard Wheater, Imperial College

Testers

The main participants in the user test programme were:

David Archer, Consultant to Jeremy Benn Associates
Alan Barr and Grace Glasgow, Kirk McClure and Morton
Don Burn, University of Waterloo, Canada
Jonathan Cooper, Owen Bramwell and Brian Darling, WS Atkins North West
Con Cunnane and Savithri Senaratne, University College Galway
Steve Dunthorne, Sir Alexander Gibb and Partners
Jim Findlay, Murray Dale, Stuart King and Birol Sokmenor, Babtie Group
Mark Futter, Montgomery Watson
Malcolm MacConnachie, Scottish Environment Protection Agency
David MacDonald, Binnie, Black and Veatch
Ian Rose, Emma Blunden and Rob Scarrott, Halcrow
Peter Spencer and David Rylands, Environment Agency
Peter Walsh, Bullen Consultants Ltd
Paul Webster and Anna Lisa Vetere Arellano, University of Birmingham
Howard Wheater and Christian Onof, Imperial College

Acknowledgements

The Flood Estimation Handbook is a product of strategic research funding at the Institute of Hydrology in the 1990s. It would not have happened without the lead shown by MAFF, in particular by Reg Purnell and David Richardson. The dedication of Advisory Group members and the testers is gratefully acknowledged. Alan Gustard (IH) is thanked for managerial assistance in a research programme that did not fit a standard mould.

General thanks go to all those who exchanged ideas with members of the team during the research programme. Those having greatest impact on the course of the research were Don Burn and Jon Hosking. A more general acknowledgement is to all earlier researchers in UK rainfall and flood frequency estimation. It would be invidious to list some and not others.

Coastlines, rivers and lake shorelines shown in the Handbook are based on material licensed from Ordnance Survey and are included with the permission of the controller of Her Majesty's Stationery Office © Crown copyright. Place names are from a gazetteer licensed from AA Developments Ltd.

More specific acknowledgements to individuals and organisations co-operating in the research are made in the relevant volume.

Volumes

1. Overview
2. Rainfall frequency estimation
3. Statistical procedures for flood frequency estimation
4. Restatement and application of the *Flood Studies Report* rainfall-runoff method
5. Catchment descriptors

Notation

The following are the symbols and abbreviations used in this volume of the Flood Estimation Handbook:

AEP	Annual exceedance probability
AREA	Catchment drainage area (km²)
B	Number of balanced resamples
BF	Baseflow ($m^3 s^{-1}$)
BFI	Baseflow index
CORINE	Co-ordination of information on environment
D	Duration (hours)
DTM	Digital terrain model
EA	Environment Agency
FARL	Index of flood attenuation due to reservoirs and lakes
FEH	Flood Estimation Handbook
FEH CD-ROM	A software package of particular relevance to the use of Volumes 2 and 5
FORGEX	Focused rainfall growth extension
FSR	Flood Studies Report
GCM	Global climate model (or general circulation model)
GEV	Generalised Extreme Value
GL	Generalised Logistic
HadCM2	Hadley Centre climate model developed in mid 1990s
HadCM3	Hadley Centre climate model developed in late 1990s
ICE	Institution of Civil Engineers
IE Australia	Institution of Engineers, Australia
IH	Institute of Hydrology
IHDTM	Institute of Hydrology digital terrain model
ITE	Institute of Terrestrial Ecology
LAG	Measure of lag time between rainfall and runoff (hours)
m	Number of years of record
M	Design life or period of interest (years)
M5	5-year return period rainfall depth (mm)
MAFF	Ministry of Agriculture Fisheries and Food
Micro-FSR	A software package relevant to use of Volume 4
N	Number of sample values, e.g. in annual maximum series
NERC	Natural Environment Research Council
OS	Ordnance Survey
PMF	Probable maximum flood ($m^3 s^{-1}$)
PMP	Probable maximum precipitation (mm)
POT	Peaks-over-threshold
Pr(.)	Symbol denoting probability
PROPWET	Index of proportion of time that soils are wet
Q	Flood flow ($m^3 s^{-1}$)
QBAR	The (arithmetic) mean annual maximum flood ($m^3 s^{-1}$)
QMED	The median annual maximum flood ($m^3 s^{-1}$)
$QMED_{rural}$	Estimate of as-rural median annual maximum flood ($m^3 s^{-1}$)
Q_t	Annual maximum flow for year t ($m^3 s^{-1}$)
Q_T	T-year return period flood ($m^3 s^{-1}$)
r	Risk probability

Overview

RMED	Median annual maximum rainfall (mm)
SAAR	1961-90 standard-period average annual rainfall (mm)
$SAAR_{4170}$	1941-70 standard-period average annual rainfall (mm)
SEPA	Scottish Environment Protection Agency
SOIL	Index of winter rainfall acceptance potential
SPR	Standard percentage runoff (%)
T	Return period or target return period (years)
T_1, T_2	Particular return periods (years)
T_{AM}	Return period on annual maximum scale (years)
T_{POT}	Return period on peaks-over-threshold scale (years)
Tp	Unit hydrograph time-to-peak (hours)
URBEXT	FEH index of fractional urban extent
USBR	United States Bureau of Reclamation
USU	Utah State University
WINFAP-FEH	A frequency analysis package for use with Volume 3
x_1, x_2	Input variables in a joint probability problem
x_T	T-year return period growth factor
X	Variable or statistic of interest
X_L	Lower percentile value of X, derived in resampling
X_{sam}	Value of X estimated from original sample
X_{true}	True value of X
X_U	Upper percentile value of X, derived in resampling
y	An output variable in a joint probability problem

Chapter 1   Introduction

1.1   Foreword

The Flood Estimation Handbook is a new publication. It represents the outcome of a 5-year research programme at the Institute of Hydrology to develop and implement new generalised procedures for rainfall and flood frequency estimation in the UK.

Flood frequency estimation is synonymous with flood risk assessment. The former focuses on estimation of the peak river flow (in $m^3 s^{-1}$) of a given frequency (i.e. rarity). The latter strives to assess the risk (i.e. probability) of a flood occurrence. Gauged records are rarely long enough to allow direct estimation of the average interval between major floods at a site, other than very approximately. This average interval defines the **return period** at which flooding occurs.

The UK is blessed with relatively extensive flood data and, by world standards, a relatively benign climate. Flood frequency estimation is, nevertheless, a persistently difficult problem in the UK. There are two main reasons for this. First, major floods are largely natural phenomena which occur highly irregularly in time. This caprice of climate makes it inherently difficult to judge flood frequency. Second, many communities, though sited close to rivers, are intolerant of flooding, and are protected by flood defences against frequent inundation of property. Consequently, the return periods of interest in UK flood design are often as long as 50 or 100 years. Even in cases where extensive gauged flood records are available, special techniques are required to estimate floods of such extreme rarity.

Specific flooding incidents, or unusual sequences of floods, can lead to great public concern and anxiety. In some cases, it may not be environmentally and economically sustainable to improve defences to further reduce the frequency of inundation. Nevertheless, flood risk assessment is required to support the decision, and to advise landowners and their insurers. The mapping of flood risk areas can also be important in the design of emergency plans to deal with a major flood catastrophe.

The Handbook seeks to contribute to improved decision-making about flood risks in the UK. Responsibilities for flood defence are summarised in ICE (1996a).

1.2   How the Handbook came about

The Handbook largely supersedes the **Flood Studies Report** (FSR) and its supplementary reports. Almost 25 years have elapsed since publication of the FSR (NERC, 1975), and organisational factors alone suggested that new guidance was required.

Updating of the FSR in 1977-1988 by eighteen Flood Studies Supplementary Reports (IH, various) became progressively more intricate and the effective dissemination of revised guidance became less assured. These trends reflected the practical difficulties of succinctly explaining updates to updates, and of ensuring that supplementary reports reached all those holding copies of earlier material. The difficulties were exacerbated by the successful penetration of FSR methods into other guides. The methods had been adopted or taught in many settings, including hydrology textbooks, engineering guides, teaching notes, and the internal documents of agencies and consultants. In consequence, stating that a design calculation was based on FSR procedures no longer carried the assurance that the most up-to-date method had been used.

There are phases in the research response to a major publication such as the Flood Studies Report. Reaction to the FSR was intense and varied. Detailed criticisms provoked further studies to review or resolve perceived weaknesses. Many training courses were held, and interactions with practitioners further stimulated research. FSR methods were adapted to special cases such as floods and reservoir safety (ICE, 1978), urbanised catchments (IH, 1979) and storm-sewer design (National Water Council, 1981). Subsequently, UK floods research became rather more diffuse. Studies considered entirely new approaches to flood frequency estimation, sought to better understand physical processes, or considered neglected topics such as the design of pumped drainage systems. In this phase, advances in flood frequency estimation led more to contract reports and research papers than to engineering guides.

Following external review (Ackers, 1992), and subsequent discussions, the Ministry of Agriculture Fisheries and Food (MAFF) adopted a new strategy for flood estimation research. Central to this strategy was the consolidation of research in rainfall and flood frequency estimation, to develop new general procedures for application in river flood defence. The Flood Estimation Handbook research programme was conceived to meet this objective, and an Advisory Group formed in 1994. The 5-year programme gained financial support from MAFF, the National Rivers Authority (subsequently, the Environment Agency), the Department of Agriculture Northern Ireland, and a consortium led by the Scottish Office.

1.3 What the Handbook intends

The Flood Estimation Handbook aims to provide clear guidance to practitioners concerned with rainfall and flood frequency estimation. Where possible, all directly relevant information is provided with, or accompanies, the Handbook, including extensive datasets in digital form. The form of presentation promotes practical use of the procedures by putting the methods first, and the supporting rationale and results second. The whole intends to be more nearly a handbook of estimation methods than a report of flood studies.

The Handbook does not dwell on the alternative methods and options that might have formed the basis of new guidance. Rather it presents a unified set of procedures for rainfall and flood frequency estimation that have quite general application. Nevertheless, various devices are employed to ensure that the user remains aware of the inherent uncertainty in estimating event magnitudes that are rarely observed. The user is exhorted to query data quality, to refine generalised estimates of flood frequency by reference to local data, to appraise historical information, and to think clearly about the use to which estimates are put.

1.4 Structure of Handbook

The Flood Estimation Handbook comprises five volumes:

1 Overview
2 Rainfall frequency estimation
3 Statistical procedures for flood frequency estimation
4 Restatement and application of the FSR rainfall-runoff method
5 Catchment descriptors

Table 1.1 gives a first indication of content.

Table 1.1 *The Flood Estimation Handbook: an indication of structure*

Overview (Volume 1)
- Guidance is provided on the choice of procedures, and the uses to which estimates are put.

Rainfall frequency estimation (Volume 2)
- A generalised procedure is provided for rainfall depth-duration-frequency estimation;
- The method is prescriptive and, in general, the incorporation of local data is not recommended.

Statistical procedures for flood frequency estimation (Volume 3)
- The T-year flood is estimated as the product of the index flood, $QMED$, and a growth factor, x_T, in single-site as well as pooled analyses;
- On urbanised catchments, flood frequency estimates are derived as if the catchment were rural and then adjusted for urbanisation;
- A special procedure is presented for growth curve estimation on permeable catchments;
- Data transfers are encouraged, with special emphasis given to transfers from donor catchments directly upstream or downstream of the subject site;
- Methods are provided to construct a design hydrograph to be consistent with the preferred estimate of the T-year peak flow.

Restatement and application of the FSR rainfall-runoff method (Volume 4)
- All information about the FSR rainfall-runoff method and its application is presented in a single volume;
- Data transfers are encouraged, with special emphasis given to transfers from donor catchments directly upstream or downstream of the subject site.

Catchment descriptors (Volume 5)
- The FEH CD-ROM provides catchment descriptors for mainland England, Wales, Scotland and Northern Ireland, and Anglesey and the Isle of Wight;
- The catchment descriptors are based on digital data, and use the IH digital terrain model (IHDTM) to define catchment boundaries;
- Descriptors for catchments draining to sites in Northern Ireland are adjusted to reflect the different mapping conventions and formats used there.

Use of the FEH is supported by software packages. A specially designed frequency analysis package, WINFAP-FEH, supports the statistical procedures of Volume 3. The Micro-FSR package is relevant to application of the FSR rainfall-runoff method (Volume 4). A third software element, the FEH CD-ROM, fulfils two functions: implementing the rainfall frequency estimation procedure (Volume 2), and presenting catchment descriptors for 4 million UK sites (see Volume 5).

The software products are likely to be updated within the lifetime of the text. Consequently, the Handbook presents only brief introductions.

1.5 Only a guidebook

Some authorities may mandate that Flood Estimation Handbook (FEH) methods be used in particular applications. Standardisation can be valuable in promoting consistency across a class of design problems. It is rarely practical for defence works to eliminate flood risk entirely, and one can never be sure that the intended level of protection is attained. When financial resources are limited, a laudable objective may be to aim for consistency from location to location rather than to carry out separate, very detailed, studies at each problem site. Use of standard procedures can also promote technical efficiency in calculating, checking and agreeing estimates.

Nevertheless, it is recommended that common sense should also be a guide. In sizing minor infrastructure works – such as culverts under forest roads – calculations based on the FEH should not necessarily take precedence over those based on simpler formulae. Inherited experience within a particular organisation provides legitimate and valuable local information.

There is a point beyond which a guidebook can become a cookbook. In the FEH, this boundary is most closely approached for the rainfall frequency estimation procedure, which is fully prescribed. In contrast, the procedures for flood frequency estimation are open-ended. There are choices to be made between methods and there is scope to improvise to make best use of the particular flood data available at, or near to, the subject site.

1.6 Structure of Volume 1

Volume 1 has two main functions. Chapters 2 to 6 introduce the Flood Estimation Handbook procedures and their use, with particular reference to the choice of method (Chapter 5) and finding data (Chapter 6). Later chapters review specific topics, such as climate change (Chapter 7) and flood risk mapping (Chapter 9). An interlude to the main text provides a reminder of potential pitfalls in practical problems.

To aid readability, some technical material is consigned to appendices. Readers may wish to note that the first section of Appendix A introduces the concept of return period. Appendix D is of a different character, presenting a bibliography of technical guidance in related aspects of flood defence.

Chapter 2   Using the Handbook

> **Cross-referencing**
>
> Cross-references to other parts of the Handbook are usually abbreviated. They are indicated by the relevant volume number preceding the chapter, section or sub-section number, with the volume number in bold (e.g. **5** 7.2 refers to Section 7.2 of Volume 5). Cross-references conventionally prefixed by Chapter, Section or § are to the current volume (e.g. §2.2 refers to the section "Maxims for flood frequency estimation")

2.1   Approaches to flood frequency estimation

The Handbook provides two main approaches to flood frequency estimation: the statistical analysis of peak flows (Volume 3) and the FSR rainfall-runoff method (Volume 4). Statistical analysis is a direct and natural approach to flood frequency estimation, and will generally be the first-choice method when there is a long record of gauged floods close to the site of interest. The FEH terminology is to refer to the site of interest as the ***subject site.***

The rainfall-runoff approach is less direct. It estimates flood frequency from rainfall frequency using a hydrological model to link rainfall to resultant runoff. The approach is conceptually appealing because it provides a model of flood formation. Moreover, it yields a hydrograph of river flow rather than just an estimate of peak flow. The rainfall-runoff approach gives scope to model important features explicitly, for example when catchment flood behaviour is influenced by reservoirs or by an unusual configuration of tributaries.

2.2   Maxims for flood frequency estimation

Six maxims summarise the Handbook viewpoint on flood frequency estimation:

1   Flood frequency is best estimated from gauged data;

2   While flood data at the subject site are of greatest value, data transfers from a nearby site, or a similar catchment, are also very useful;

3   Estimation of key variables – such as the index-flood ($QMED$, Volume 3) or the unit hydrograph time-to-peak (Tp, Volume 4) – from catchment descriptors alone, should be a method of last resort; some kind of data transfer will usually be feasible and preferable;

4   The most appropriate choice of method is a matter of experience, and may be influenced by the requirement of the study and the nature of the catchment; most importantly, it will be influenced by the available data;

5   In some cases, a hybrid method – combining estimates by statistical and rainfall-runoff approaches – will be appropriate;

6   There is always more information; an estimate based only on readily available data may be shown to be suspect by a more enquiring analyst.

Although these maxims are stated formally only here, they underlie both the recommendations about choice of method (Chapter 5) and the suggestions for finding data (Chapter 6). The maxims should be borne in mind when using the

D.W. Reed & H.A. Houghton-Carr   **5**

statistical and rainfall-runoff procedures for flood frequency estimation presented in Volumes 3 and 4.

2.3 Data transfers

A data transfer is recommended when the subject site is ungauged. The term is a shorthand description for the process of adjusting a generalised estimate at the subject site by reference to how the generalised procedure performs at a nearby gauged site, or a more distant gauged catchment that is thought to be hydrologically similar. The rationale for such a transfer of information is the relative imprecision of generalised estimates (i.e. from catchment descriptors) compared to specific estimates made from gauged data.

The Handbook reinforces Flood Studies Report (NERC, 1975) recommendations to analyse 'local data', by distinguishing two kinds of catchment from which data may be transferred:

- A ***donor catchment*** is a local catchment offering gauged data that are particularly relevant to flood estimation at the subject site. The ideal donor catchment is one sited just upstream or downstream of the subject site. More typically, it will be sited some distance upstream or downstream, draining an area rather smaller or larger than the subject catchment. A similar-sized catchment on an adjacent tributary can also make a good donor if the physiography and land-use of the two catchments are broadly similar.

- An ***analogue catchment*** is a more distant gauged catchment that is sufficiently similar to the subject catchment to make a transfer of information worthwhile. Judging a suitable analogue requires hydrological understanding and experience.

Advice on the choice of a donor/analogue catchments is given in §3.3.

2.4 Summary of resources

Effective use of the Flood Estimation Handbook draws on resources of three types: text, data and software. These are summarised in Figures 2.1 to 2.3.

2.4.1 Text

The Handbook presents three main sets of procedures: one for rainfall frequency estimation (Volume 2) and two for flood frequency estimation (Volumes 3 and 4). Volume 1 has a co-ordinating and sweeping-up role, while Volume 5 presents digital catchment data supporting the main procedures.

2.4.2 Data

The main data resources accompanying the text are indicated in Figure 2.2.

Flood data

Summaries of flood peak data are presented in appendices to Volume 3. The FEH flood peak datasets accompany Volume 3 (Statistical procedures for flood frequency estimation) on the ***flood data CD-ROM***. This provides a frozen record of the flood peak data used in the research underlying Volume 3, and is a convenient source of flood data for teaching and incidental research.

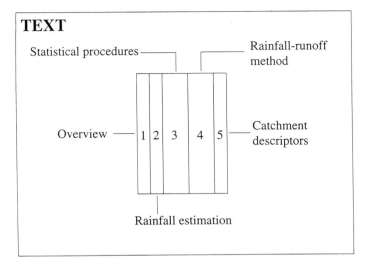

Figure 2.1   *Text resources*

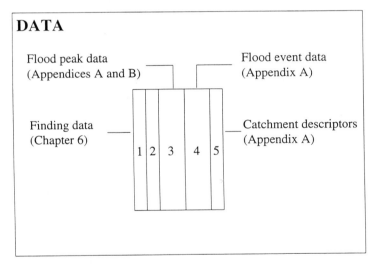

Figure 2.2   *Data resources*

The FEH flood peak datasets are also supplied with **WINFAP-FEH**, the frequency analysis package which supports use of the Volume 3 procedures. Though initially identical, the WINFAP-FEH versions of the datasets will evolve over time. They will be updated or superseded when datasets are revised and extended by, or on behalf of, UK gauging authorities (see §6.2). Users of the Volume 3 procedures should check the FEH web pages (see §2.8) to ensure that they are using the most up-to-date and reliable versions of UK flood peak data.

Summaries of the FEH flood event data are presented in an appendix to Volume 4, and on the floppy disk accompanying that volume.

Catchment descriptors

The digital catchment descriptors used in the estimation methods are supplied in several ways. Twenty descriptors for each of 1000 gauged catchments are tabulated in the appendix to Volume 5, and also included on the flood data CD-ROM. With minor exceptions, these document the descriptors used in the FEH research.

Catchment descriptors for UK sites, gauged and ungauged, can be obtained from the companion **FEH CD-ROM**, available from the Institute of Hydrology. The initial version supplies catchment descriptors for all mainland sites in England, Wales, Scotland and Northern Ireland – plus sites in Anglesey and the Isle of Wight – which drain an area of 0.5 km² or greater. The FEH CD-ROM provides software to help the user locate the site of interest within IHDTM, the Institute of Hydrology digital terrain model. This **subject-site locator** tool illustrates the site location and catchment layout relative to major drainage paths, urban areas, and FEH gauging stations. An image of the catchment boundary is displayed and the required catchment descriptor values retrieved.

Digital catchment data, and digital maps of catchments, should be seen as complementing information from paper maps. Users should always refer to OS maps of an appropriate scale to the size of the catchment, both to verify that the subject site has been correctly located, and to check for unusual catchment features. In some cases, it may also be appropriate to refer to paper maps of soils, geology or hydrogeology.

2.4.3 Software

The FEH procedures are supported by three software packages (see Figure 2.3). Use of the rainfall frequency estimation procedure (Volume 2) is relatively straight-forward. The relevant software tools and parameter values are given in the rainfall frequency part of the **FEH CD-ROM**. Rainfall frequency calculations can be performed either for a specific point or for a typical point within a catchment. A further option allows application of an areal reduction factor to yield frequency estimates for catchment rainfall. Tools provide the rainfall depth for a given return

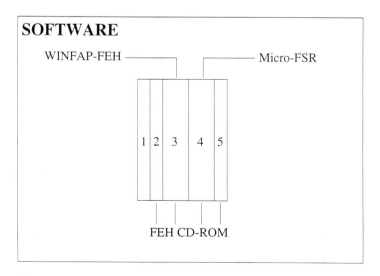

Figure 2.3   *Software resources*

period and duration, and the return period corresponding to a given rainfall depth and duration.

Use of the statistical procedures for flood frequency estimation (Volume 3) is supported by **WINFAP-FEH**. This frequency analysis package implements the Volume 3 procedures for single-site and pooled frequency analyses.

Use of the FSR rainfall-runoff method (Volume 4) is supported by **Micro-FSR**. At the time of publication, the most recent version (Version 3) is not fully compatible with the Handbook. In particular, there is a requirement to update Micro-FSR so that:

- Rainfall frequency estimation can use the Volume 2 procedure;

- Unit hydrograph time-to-peak (Tp) can be estimated from digital catchment descriptors.

It is possible that an updated version of Micro-FSR may specialise more exclusively on supporting the FSR rainfall-runoff method, and provide software for flood event analysis. Pending such development, code is supplied for unit hydrograph derivation (both for single events and by event superposition) and for unit hydrograph transformation by the extended S-curve method. Code is also supplied for reservoir flood routing. The relevant source programs – written in FORTRAN – accompany Volume 4 on the **miscellaneous floppy disk**. These miscellaneous programs are offered without warranty or support.

2.5   Duty of care

Despite the opportunities for data transfers, and for combining estimates, there will still be times when the experienced analyst feels constrained by instructions to follow the Handbook: whether these are explicit or implied. In such cases, it is recommended that the user records the departures openly and clearly. While the Handbook is intended to give detailed guidance it cannot absolve the user from a duty of care. For example, it is the user's responsibility to provide enough information to allow estimates to be understood and validated by a suitably experienced third party.

Where public safety is at risk (see Chapter 10), it is essential that the superintending engineer verifies that calculations have been carried out correctly. The greater automation afforded by the FEH is intended to allow more thoughtful and discriminating flood estimates, rather than to promote flood estimation by the non-specialist. Automation increases the user's obligation to take care, and, in cases of doubt, to seek advice from a suitably qualified expert.

2.6   Digital catchment data

The Handbook is pioneering the use of digital catchment data in flood frequency estimation. The delineation of boundaries via the IH Digital Terrain Model is central to this. Catchment descriptors are supplied on the FEH CD-ROM (see **5** 7).

Catchment boundaries based on digital terrain data are inevitably approximate and differences can be important. Cases where discrepancies are most likely to arise include: small catchments, areas of low relief, braided rivers, and catchments where natural drainage paths have been diverted. Catchment boundaries are readily influenced by drainage works and by embankments: for example, those associated with flood defence, mineral extraction, agricultural practice, urbanisation, canals, railways and highways. It is essential that the user confirms that the boundary based on digital data adequately portrays the effective catchment. Boundaries inferred from contours on paper maps can also be problematic, and a site survey may be necessary.

2.7 Learning from mistakes

Rainfall frequency estimation and flood frequency estimation are relatively subtle tasks, providing scope to tackle the wrong question or to answer the right question by the wrong method. An interlude to this volume takes a sideways look at ways in which estimates sometimes go wrong. It is inspired by a similar interlude in Acton (1970). It is hoped that this candidness encourages users to share what they come across in their travels through flood frequency estimation: the good as well as the bad, the ingenious as well as the ingenuous. The motive is simple: "… in order to learn from previous mistakes and oversights and to preclude similar eventualities in the future" (Murphy, 1993).

The focus throughout the Handbook is on UK circumstances and practice, and some parts of Volume 1 – not least the interlude – inevitably appear parochial when compared with the more socially important flood estimation problems faced elsewhere. Litigious and blaming attitudes are a feature of western culture at the millennium, from which the flood defence industry is not exempt. When serious flood damage occurs, it is rather easy to blame the hydrologist: flood frequency estimation is inherently uncertain, and there is inevitably greater scope to under-estimate than overestimate. Yet a good hydrologist is no less a professional than the good engineer or hydraulician. There is material in the interlude that may help the hydrologist avoid the mire.

2.8 Revision policy

Subject to funding, it is expected that parts of the Handbook will be revised, based on user feedback, specialist comment and additional research. It is anticipated that revisions will take the form of amended paragraphs, sections or chapters. Revisions are likely to be announced and made available by electronic media rather than in paper form. The addresses of World Wide Web pages providing official update information for the Flood Estimation Handbook will be advertised through the Institute of Hydrology's homepage: **http://www.nwl.ac.uk/ih.**

Chapter 3   Using the Handbook procedures

3.1 Scope

The scope of the Handbook procedures reflects the rainfall, flood and catchment data used in their formulation and calibration.

3.1.1 Geographical limits

The various estimation procedures are generally applicable to sites throughout the UK. Initially, the procedures are fully implemented for application in mainland England, Wales, Scotland and Northern Ireland, plus Anglesey and the Isle of Wight. For brevity, this amalgam is sometimes referred to as "mainland UK".

3.1.2 Catchment limits

The frequency estimation procedures can be used on any catchment, gauged or ungauged, that drains an area of at least 0.5 km². The flood estimation procedures can be applied on smaller catchments only where the catchment is gauged and offers ample flood peak or flood event data.

The FSR rainfall-runoff method (Volume 4) is less suitable for application to catchments larger than about 1000 km². This reflects a selection criterion used in calibration of the method (NERC, 1975), which in turn reflected a concern that UK flood-producing conditions (i.e. antecedent wetness and storm rainfall) span very large catchments only infrequently.

Floodplain storage is known to influence flood frequency in the middle and lower reaches of larger UK rivers. An unresolved issue is to develop an effective index of floodplain storage, and to consider its use in flood frequency estimation. It is therefore necessary to be wary when applying procedures to floodplain-dominated rivers.

Box 3.1   Very small catchments

Catchment descriptors are provided for all sites draining an area of 0.5 km² (50 hectares) or greater. This lower limit reflects the facts that:

- Very small catchments are poorly represented in the datasets used to calibrate the models for estimating flood frequency from catchment descriptors;
- Digital terrain and thematic data may not be well resolved on very small catchments.

While inconveniencing users wishing to estimate floods on catchments only slightly smaller than 0.5 km², the limit puts an important brake on inappropriate applications to very small catchments.

3.1.3 Urbanisation limits

Both the statistical flood estimation procedures (Volume 3) and the rainfall-runoff method (Volume 4) include allowances for effects arising from catchment urbanisation. The procedures can be used to estimate flood frequency at current-day levels of urbanisation. With caution, the rainfall-runoff method can also be used to assess the incremental effect of urban development. However, for reasons introduced in §8.3 (and elaborated in **3** 18), the urban adjustment model in the statistical approach must not be so used. To do so would lead to systematic underestimation of the aggravating effect of urbanisation on flood frequency.

None of the flood estimation procedures is recommended for use on exceptionally heavily urbanised catchments. A suitable test is to query applications when the FEH descriptor of urban extent, *URBEXT*, exceeds 0.5.

3.1.4 Frequency limits

Volume 2 presents a general procedure for estimating rainfall depth-duration-frequency for any site or catchment. The procedure is intended principally for durations between one hour and eight days, and return periods between 2 and 2000 years. With caution, it can be extrapolated for use at somewhat shorter durations (e.g. 30 or 15 minutes), at somewhat longer durations (e.g. 12 or 16 days), and at longer return periods (e.g. 5000 or 10000 years).

Volumes 3 and 4 present alternative methods for flood frequency estimation for any catchment, gauged or ungauged. The statistical procedures (Volume 3) are intended principally for use for return periods between 2 and 200 years. The rainfall-runoff method (Volume 4) is applicable to a somewhat wider range of return periods. In conjunction with Volume 2, it can be used to estimate floods for return periods between 2 and 2000 years. Because of the difficulty of validating the rainfall frequency estimation procedure at very long return periods, applications of the rainfall-runoff method to estimate 5000 and 10000-year floods require circumspection. In conjunction with estimates of the ***probable maximum precipitation***, the rainfall-runoff method can be applied to estimate the ***probable maximum flood*** (see **4** 4).

3.2 Basic concepts

3.2.1 Patterns in UK river flooding

Except in tidal estuaries, there is no strong regularity (i.e. periodicity) in UK river flooding. Floods occur irregularly, with the gap between major events often long but occasionally short. There are, however, patterns in flood occurrences: most notably, seasonal effects.

With few exceptions, the dominant UK flood season is winter. This reflects the strong influence of soil wetness on flood formation. In winter, soil wetness conditions are typically conducive to flood generation when heavy rainfall occurs. In summer, soils are often dry, there being a ***soil moisture deficit.*** This means that heavy rainfall may be absorbed, thus suppressing flood formation.

Antecedent wetness conditions are less relevant on heavily urbanised catchments, and on certain shallow-soiled steep catchments. The dominant flood season in such catchments may be summer, reflecting the seasonal preference of intense thunderstorms.

The tendency for wetter and drier epochs is a feature of global and regional climates. Thus some sequences of years are unusually 'rich' or 'poor' in terms of flood occurrences (see §7.3). This natural variability is an obstacle to reliable flood frequency estimation, and unusual successions of flooding can lead to misconceptions about flood risk.

3.2.2 Risk and return period

Risk is a probability that something undesired occurs. Flood risk assessment and flood frequency estimation are intimately related (see §1.1).

The return period of a given flood is the average interval between floods of this magnitude or greater. Because there is no regularity in river flooding (see §3.2.1), the key word in the above definition is "average". Variations of the basic definition are given in Appendix A. Section A.1 also confirms the meaning of the T-year flood; it is the flood magnitude that has a return period of T years.

Section A.2 introduces the risk equation. This relates risk to return period, by specifying the risk, r, of the T-year flood being exceeded in a period of M years:

$$r = 1 - (1 - 1/T)^M \tag{3.1}$$

Here, M may denote the intended design life of the flood defence structure.

3.2.3 Catchment boundaries

The catchment boundary defines the area which potentially contributes to river flow at the subject site. In flood applications, the catchment boundary is generally defined by topography, although embankments and drainage diversions may be important (see §2.6). Catchments with highly permeable strata – e.g. chalk catchments or those with natural underground (i.e. karstic) drainage – present particular problems.

In difficult cases, catchment layout and properties are best assessed from detailed maps and site survey. The provision of digital catchment descriptors via the FEH CD-ROM is intended to complement the traditional use of a variety of paper maps, both topographic and specialist.

Warning

Catchment boundaries derived from paper maps, or from the digital terrain model underpinning the FEH CD-ROM, may not represent the effective drainage area for flood runoff. Where there is scope for the drainage area to be under or over-represented – and a 5% error would certainly be considered unacceptable – the user should refer to contour data at least as detailed as those shown (in Great Britain) on OS 1:25 000 maps. In cases of doubt, the site should be visited and, if appropriate, surveyed. Fenland districts present particular difficulty. In some cases, detailed local knowledge may be required to ascertain the direction in which floodwater would drain in a major event.

3.3 Selecting donor and analogue catchments

The Handbook recommends that data transfers from gauged sites are used to refine flood estimates at ungauged sites. Section 2.3 introduces the concepts of donor and analogue catchments. A donor catchment is a local catchment offering gauged data that are particularly relevant to flood estimation at the subject site. An analogue catchment is a more distant gauged catchment that is thought to be hydrologically similar to the subject site.

The FEH CD-ROM (see §2.4.2) displays gauge positions to help users to identify potential donor catchments. However, it is important to check locally for additional gauged catchments not in the FEH flood datasets. While designed principally to support the statistical procedures for flood frequency estimation, the WINFAP-FEH software (see §2.4.3) provides diagnostic displays of catchment similarity, and brief descriptions of gauging stations and their catchments. These are helpful in confirming donor-catchment suitability or in searching for a possible analogue catchment. To benefit from this facility, it is worth applying the statistical method on an exploratory basis, even in cases where the final estimate is to be based on the rainfall-runoff method.

Box 3.2 Choosing a donor or analogue catchment

The search for a donor catchment is confined to gauges close to the subject catchment. When choosing a donor, the catchment descriptor values should indicate broad similarity. Only small differences should be tolerated for soils and wetness variables, e.g. differing by no more than a factor of about 1.1. Greater differences can be allowed in terms of catchment size: generally tolerating a factor of two difference and – where the donor site lies directly upstream or downstream of the subject site – sometimes a factor of five difference. A donor catchment is sought when the subject site is ungauged or has only a short record.

An analogue catchment is sought when the subject site is ungauged and there is no suitable donor catchment. The assessment of hydrological similarity should be both strict and comprehensive. The subject and analogue catchments should be similar in terms of all descriptor values, and in terms of any special feature.

A prerequisite is that a donor or analogue catchment must offer gauged data of good quality.

Extreme caution is required if the subject catchment is urbanised or includes a major reservoir. Similarity in terms of *URBEXT* and *FARL* values – the FEH indices of urban extent and flood attenuation due to reservoirs and lakes – may not guarantee similarity in terms of urbanisation and reservoir effects. The effect of urbanisation on flood frequency depends on many factors – including soil characteristics and drainage practice – and can be particularly variable for small catchments.

Chapter 4   Principal new features

Some readers will be familiar with procedures based on the Flood Studies Report (FSR). This chapter highlights the principal new features of the Flood Estimation Handbook (FEH).

Overview (Volume 1)

- Particular concerns, such as flood risk mapping and climate change, are reviewed;

- An interlude gives a candid account of pitfalls, and an appendix points to technical guidance in related flood defence topics.

Rainfall frequency estimation (Volume 2)

- The 2-year rainfall depth (*RMED*), rather than the 5-year rainfall depth (*M5*), is used as the index variable;

- Users obtain estimates from an overarching model of rainfall depth-duration-frequency rather than in a succession of calculation steps;

- The parameters of the rainfall frequency model are provided digitally on a 1-km grid, rather than on paper maps at 1:625 000 scale;

- Mapping of the index rainfall for key durations reflects orography and position by geostatistical analysis rather than by subjective interpolation;

- The estimation of rare rainfall depths is based on the FORGEX method; this gives precedence to rainfall extremes observed close to the subject site, while pooling data from further afield when extending the growth curve to long return periods;

- The rainfall frequency estimates show greater local variations, with generally increased depths in parts of eastern England.

Statistical procedures for flood frequency estimation (Volume 3)

- The median annual flood *QMED*, rather than the mean annual flood *QBAR*, is used as the index variable; *QMED* is the 2-year flood;

- In the absence of flood peak data, *QMED* is estimated from catchment descriptors based on digital data rather than derived manually from maps;

- Pooling of flood peak data for growth curve derivation is flexible rather than fixed, and is tailored to the subject site; stations are selected to form part of the pooling-group according to catchment similarity rather than according to their Hydrometric Area;

- Catchment similarity is initially judged in terms of size, wetness and soils; flood seasonality, assessed from peaks-over-threshold (POT) flood data, is one of several methods by which the hydrological similarity of gauged catchments is reviewed;

- Frequency estimation is based on L-moment methods throughout; these methods are also used for inspecting pooling-groups, and testing their homogeneity;

- The Generalised Logistic (GL) distribution rather than the Generalised Extreme Value (GEV) distribution is the default recommendation to describe annual maximum floods in the UK.

Restatement and application of the FSR rainfall-runoff method (Volume 4)

- In the absence of flood event data, the parameters of the rainfall-runoff model are estimated from descriptors based on digital data rather than derived manually from maps;

- Explicit guidance is given on application of the rainfall-runoff method to catchments with tributaries that are disparate in soil type or land use.

Catchment descriptors (Volume 5)

- Estimates of urban extent, *URBEXT*, derive from satellite data and provide greater resolution, identifying non-built-up areas within urban settlements; in consequence, *URBEXT* values are numerically smaller than estimates of urban fraction made from OS 1:50 000 maps;

- Estimates of *URBEXT* based on ITE's Land Cover Map have a nominal date-stamp of 1990; the generalised models have been calibrated to allow for typical urban expansion during the period of record;

- The *FARL* index of flood attenuation due to reservoirs and lakes is introduced; the index reflects the size and location of water bodies shown on OS 1:50 000 maps relative to DTM-based drainage paths to the subject site;

- The *PROPWET* index of soil moisture status is introduced; this index reflects the proportion of the time that soils are saturated, based on estimates of soil moisture deficit.

Chapter 5   Which method to use

5.1   Introduction

The Handbook presents two approaches to flood frequency estimation: one based on statistical analysis of flood peak data (Volume 3), the other on the FSR rainfall-runoff method (Volume 4). This chapter gives advice on the choice of method to apply to a given problem.

Rainfall frequency estimation is relevant to flood estimation by the rainfall-runoff method. The Volume 2 procedure is simple to use, and can be applied either to estimate the *D*-hour rainfall depth of a given rarity or to estimate the rarity of a given *D*-hour depth. An extension allows calculations to be made for catchment-average rainfall depths. The general recommendation is that rainfall frequency estimates should **not** be adjusted by reference to local rainfall data. Thus, estimates provided by the procedure are unique and all users should obtain the same results.

The choice of method for flood frequency estimation is both complex and subjective. Different users will obtain different results, by bringing different data and experience to bear. Though a difficult read, this chapter is important in setting down some of the principles and ideas to follow when choosing a method. Box 5.1 explains why the choice of method is important.

Box 5.1   Why the choice of method matters

Flood frequency estimation is important. The estimate usually drives the size or feasibility of a flood alleviation scheme, or determines the assessed risk of inundation.

Flood frequency estimation is uncertain. The FEH suggests that a gauged record twice as long as the target return period is required to be confident that a statistical analysis of flood peaks provides a good estimate of the true flood frequency. In practical cases, the statistical approach (Volume 3) calls for data to be pooled from a group of catchments judged to be similar to the subject catchment. However elegant, a pooled analysis will not always represent flood behaviour at the subject site faithfully. Flood estimates by the FSR rainfall-runoff method (Volume 4) are typically rather more uncertain, in part because of the assumptions necessary in the 'design event' approach to flood frequency estimation.

In view of the above, it is important to reduce the uncertainty in the statistical and rainfall-runoff approaches by fully incorporating gauged data into the methods, and by exercising hydrological judgement. This is advisable in all circumstances.

5.2   Preliminary considerations

Two sets of procedures are provided for flood frequency estimation: statistical procedures (Volume 3) and the rainfall-runoff method (Volume 4). In flood frequency estimation, the recommendation is to adjust generalised estimates (i.e. those based on catchment descriptors rather than gauged data) by data transfers from nearby or similar catchments (see §2.3). The type of gauged data available may determine the choice of method. In addition, the choice of method sometimes interacts with the type of catchment and the purpose for which the flood estimate is required. Thus, there are many possibilities and considerable judgement is required in choosing a solution method. Because practical problems tend to be multi-faceted, the less experienced user is encouraged to consider all the material in Chapter 5 before choosing a method or methods. Preliminary questions to ask are:

- Is the subject site gauged?
- Is there a gauged site nearby that will make a useful donor catchment?
- Can the flood series be brought up-to-date?
- Is one approach to be favoured, or should the final flood frequency estimate be a hybridisation of estimates by the statistical and rainfall-runoff methods?

5.3 Choice of method within the statistical approach

The statistical approach constructs the flood frequency curve Q_T as the product of the index flood $QMED$ and the growth curve x_T. The choice of method for estimating $QMED$ depends on the length of gauged record, as summarised in Table 5.1. Where the record length is a lot shorter than 30 years, a period-of-record correction (see **3** 20) is recommended. This seeks to insulate the $QMED$ estimate from the effects of climatic fluctuation.

Table 5.1   Recommended method for estimating index flood, QMED

Length of record	QMED estimation method
< 2 years	Data transfer from donor/analogue catchment
2 to 13 years	From peaks-over-threshold (POT) data
> 13 years	As median of annual maxima

The recommended method for estimating the growth curve x_T depends on both the length of gauged record and the target return period T. This is the return period for which the flood frequency estimate is principally required. The guidelines are summarised in Tables 5.2 and 5.3. The choice between tables depends on T. Table 5.3 is relevant to most river flood design problems, where the target return period is typically longer than 27 years.

Table 5.2   Recommended methods for growth curve estimation: when T ≤ 27 years

Length of record	Site analysis	Pooled analysis [†]	Shorthand description
< $T/2$ years	No	Yes	Pooled analysis
$T/2$ to T years	For confirmation	Yes	Pooled analysis prevails
T to $2T$ years	Yes	Yes [‡]	Joint (site and pooled) analysis
> $2T$ years	Yes	For confirmation [‡]	Site analysis prevails

[†] Size of pooling-group chosen to provide $5T$ station-years of record
[‡] Subject site excluded from pooled analysis

Table 5.3 *Recommended methods for growth curve estimation: when T > 27 years*

Length of record	Site analysis	Pooled analysis [†]	Shorthand description
< 14 years	No	Yes	Pooled analysis
14 to *T* years	For confirmation	Yes	Pooled analysis prevails
T to 2*T* years	Yes	Yes [‡]	Joint (site and pooled) analysis
> 2*T* years	Yes	For confirmation [‡]	Site analysis prevails

[†] Size of pooling-group chosen to provide 5*T* station-years of record
[‡] Subject site excluded from pooled analysis

In the FEH procedures, growth curve estimation is from flood data in annual maximum form. In Tables 5.2 and 5.3, "for confirmation" means that the analysis is undertaken for comparison only; unless there are exceptional factors, the other analysis should prevail. A detail – shown in a footnote – concerns whether the subject site is included in its own pooling-group for growth curve derivation. In essence, if the site record is long enough for the site analysis to play a direct role in growth curve estimation in its own right, the site is excluded from the pooled analysis. However, such cases will not arise very often, because the gauged record is rarely as long as the target return period. Typically, the growth curve will be based on a pooled analysis.

5.4   Choice of method within the rainfall-runoff approach

The rainfall-runoff method uses a unit hydrograph/losses model with three parameters. One parameter controls the temporal characteristics of the runoff response to rainfall: the unit hydrograph time-to-peak, Tp. A second parameter influences the volumetric characteristics of the runoff response: the standard percentage runoff, SPR. The third parameter represents the river-flow prior to the flood event, termed the baseflow, BF: this parameter is important only on highly permeable catchments. Wherever possible, estimates of Tp and SPR should be based on gauged data rather than catchment descriptors.

Table 5.4 *Recommended method for parameter estimation in rainfall-runoff method*

Choice	Method	Data required	Parameters estimated or adjusted
1st	Flood event analysis	Rainfall and flow data for at least five flood events	Tp, SPR, BF
2nd	Indirect analysis of gauged data	Rainfall and water level data for at least five flood events	Tp from LAG
		Flow data for at least one year	SPR from BFI
3rd	Data transfer	Flood event analysis for donor/analogue catchment	Tp, SPR, BF
4th	Data transfer	Indirect analysis of gauged data for donor/analogue catchment	Tp from LAG and/or SPR from BFI
5th	Last resort	Catchment descriptors	Tp, SPR, BF

5.5 Factors influencing the choice between statistical and rainfall-runoff approaches

The statistical and rainfall-runoff approaches can be used in most situations. This section highlights cases where one of the approaches is specifically preferred. Guidance on reconciling estimates from the two approaches is given in §5.6.

5.5.1 Type of problem

- The rainfall-runoff method should generally be used for **reservoir flood estimation** (see Chapter 10 and **4** 8). Guidance by the Institution of Civil Engineers implies that statistical flood frequency estimation should not be used in dam-safety appraisal (**4** 8.1.2). A possible exception is for dams that the guide (ICE, 1996b) places in Category D: "Special cases where no loss of life can be foreseen as a result of a breach and very limited additional flood damage will be caused."

- Estimation of the **Probable Maximum Flood** (PMF) requires use of the rainfall-runoff method (**4** 4). An upper bound on flood flows estimated by fitting a statistical distribution should **never** be interpreted as an estimate of the PMF.

- The rainfall-runoff method is favoured for problems involving **storage routing** because it provides a design hydrograph. This makes it possible to examine storage and overspill effects in floodplains, reservoirs, balancing ponds etc. Hybrid methods (**3** 10 and **4** 7.3.1) are relevant when use of the statistical approach is predisposed by other factors (see below).

5.5.2 Type of catchment

- The statistical approach should generally be used for large catchments, e.g. when the drainage area exceeds 1000 km². The concept of a catchment-wide design storm is less realistic for large catchments, making the rainfall-runoff approach less appropriate.

- The rainfall-runoff approach is favoured when subcatchments are disparate (**4** 9.2). Tributary catchments to the subject site may differ markedly in their soil properties or degree of urbanisation. An impounding reservoir within the catchment may be large enough to exert a strong unnatural influence on the flood regime at the subject site.

- Use of the permeable-catchment variation (**3** 19) of the statistical approach is favoured when the catchment is highly permeable.

5.5.3 Type of data

- The statistical approach is favoured when the gauged record is longer than two or three years.

- The rainfall-runoff method is favoured when there is no continuous flow record but rainfall and flow data (or rainfall and water level data) are available for five or more flood events (**4** 2).

5.6 Reconciling estimates from the statistical and rainfall-runoff approaches

When the subject site has ample flood peak data to allow a direct estimate of *QMED*, this should not in general be overruled by an estimate from the rainfall-runoff method. In such cases, the estimate by the statistical approach should be preferred at the shorter return periods (e.g. in the 2- to 10-year range).

More typically, the subject site is ungauged, and there is an uncomfortably large difference between the catchment-descriptor estimates of flood frequency obtained by the two approaches. The recommended procedure is to adjust *QMED* (in the statistical approach), and *Tp* and *SPR* (in the rainfall-runoff method), based on how the catchment-descriptor models of these variables perform on a donor/analogue catchment (see §5.3 and §5.4).

It is reassuring if the effect of the adjustments is to draw the statistical and rainfall-runoff estimates closer together. It is also informative if the adjustments are synergetic, i.e. if the data transfer increases (or decreases) the flood frequency estimate uniformly in both approaches. In some cases, however, the effect of applying local data will be found to increase the gap between the statistical and rainfall-runoff estimates, or to move the estimates in opposing directions.

It is currently beyond the state of the art to develop formal estimates of the uncertainty of estimates by these recommended methods. Some value judgement therefore has to be placed on the relative merits of estimates by the statistical and rainfall-runoff methods. Individual circumstances differ. However, because it is based on a much larger database of flood events, and has been more directly calibrated to reproduce flood frequency on UK catchments, estimates by the statistical procedure will often be favoured. In other cases, an intermediate estimate will be adopted.

Where a design hydrograph is required, various hybrid methods (see **3** 10 and **4** 7.3.1) can be used to derive a hydrograph with a peak value that matches the preferred flood frequency estimate. However, in the design of flood storage reservoirs, it is usually essential to recast the preferred flood peak estimate into the rainfall-runoff method (see **3** 10.2). This allows due account to be taken of the attenuating effect of reservoir storage, which heightens sensitivity to long-duration floods (see **4** 8). As an aside to this discussion, it is important to note that less formal storage of water (e.g. on floodplains) can also present a 'reservoir effect'.

5.7 Choice of method when the catchment is urbanised

Table 5.5. distinguishes six categories of catchment urbanisation defined according to *URBEXT,* the FEH index of urban extent. This must not be confused with the index of urbanisation used in the Flood Studies Report (see **5** 6.5).

Table 5.5 *Categories of catchment urbanisation*

Class name	Range of URBEXT	Notes
Essentially rural	0.000 – 0.025	
Slightly urbanised	0.025 – 0.050	Rural version of rainfall-runoff method applies
Moderately urbanised	0.050 – 0.125	
Heavily urbanised	0.125 – 0.250	
Very heavily urbanised	0.250 – 0.500	Urban version of rainfall-runoff method applies
Extremely heavily urbanised	0.500 – 1.000	Do not apply FEH methods

Statistical approach

In the statistical approach, the flood frequency estimate for an urbanised catchment is obtained in stages. First, the index flood and the growth curve are derived as if the catchment were rural. Both are then adjusted for catchment urbanisation, before being multiplied together to estimate the flood frequency curve (see **3** 18). On essentially rural catchments (i.e. with $URBEXT \leq 0.025$), the adjustment for urbanisation can be waived.

Rainfall-runoff approach

Allowances for catchment urbanisation are built into the rainfall-runoff method (Volume 4). Two cases are distinguished, according to the degree of catchment urbanisation: slight to moderate ($URBEXT \leq 0.125$) or heavy ($URBEXT > 0.125$). The unit hydrograph/losses model is the same in both cases; however, a different set of *design inputs* is used for heavily urbanised catchments (see **4** 3.2).

Box 5.3 Transferring estimates from a donor catchment that is urbanised

Where the subject site is ungauged but there is a useful donor site nearby, an estimate can exceptionally be transferred from one urbanised catchment to another. In this context, a useful donor site is one draining a hydrologically similar, and similarly urbanised, catchment.

In such a case, it can be helpful to unravel the effect of urbanisation before transferring the estimate. The first step is to derive a best estimate of flood frequency at the donor site. Then the relevant urban adjustment is applied in reverse, to estimate the as-rural flood frequency curve at the donor site. Next, the estimate is transferred from the donor site to the subject site, as if both catchments were rural. Finally, the estimate at the subject site is re-adjusted for urbanisation. This approach can be applied to estimates by the statistical procedure or by the rainfall-runoff method. However, the adjustment model used to represent the urban effect at the subject site must be the same as that used to remove the urban effect at the donor site.

Particular circumspection is warranted before making such a transfer. It should be attempted only when:

- The gauged data at the donor site are of good quality;
- The donor and subject catchments are hydrologically similar in their rural condition;
- Urbanisation and drainage provision in the catchments are of similar character, and their layout relative to soil types is similar.

Judging the incremental effect of urban development

In development-control applications (see Chapter 8), it is often desired to assess the incremental effect of an urban development on flood risk locally. This most often concerns small or very small drainage areas, for which gauged data are sparse. Flood frequency estimation is particular uncertain because such small catchments are not well represented in the datasets on which the generalised methods have been calibrated (see Table 8.1).

Flood frequency estimates on urbanised catchments derived using the statistical approach represent only the **net** effect of urbanisation: i.e. the residual effect that flood attenuation measures have typically failed to cater for. Thus, the FEH statistical approach cannot be used to assess the incremental effect of development. Because allowances for catchment urbanisation are more fully integrated into the method, with caution the rainfall-runoff method can be used to assess the incremental effect of development. However, an apparently small incremental effect does not justify neglecting practical measures to reduce or offset the increased runoff arising from development.

5.8   Additional possibilities

Less obvious situations arise when an unusually damaging flood event has occurred. Can a satisfactory assessment of event rarity be made from rainfall data (see **4 5**)? If so, can this help to refine the flood frequency estimation? Other questions concern the availability and relevance of historical flood data, e.g.:

- What is already known about the river's flood history?
- Can this be researched more fully?
- How reliable is the historical information and how is it to be interpreted?
- Is the flood history broadly supportive of the preferred flood frequency estimate?
- If not, how should the preferred estimate be adjusted?

Appendix C encourages qualitative use of historical flood data in confirming or querying flood frequency estimates. It is always helpful to be aware of previous studies of the flooding problem. These may point to important site-specific factors and to useful sources of additional information. However, conformity with a previous study is not a sufficient reason for choosing a particular solution method.

Box 5.4 Checklist when choosing a method of flood frequency estimation

- Objectives of the study;
- Flood data at subject site;
- Flood data at nearby **donor** sites;
- Flood data for similar, but more distant, **analogue** catchments; ·
- Other relevant data (e.g. rainfall, soil moisture deficit, ...);
- Background flood history.

Chapter 6 Finding data

6.1 Extreme rainfall data

The FEH recommendation is that rainfall depth-duration-frequency relationships be estimated using the generalised procedure presented in Volume 2. In exceptional cases, the user may wish to obtain and analyse extreme rainfall depths (e.g. daily or hourly totals) for a particular site or locality.

The research behind Volume 2 used annual maximum series abstracted or gathered from many sources. Copies of these data have been passed to the UK Met. Office at Bracknell, under a tripartite (Met. Office/Institute of Hydrology/ National Rivers Authority) Memorandum of Understanding agreed at the outset of the research. Under these and other conditions, the Institute of Hydrology is not allowed to communicate rainfall data supplied by the Met. Office.

The annual maximum rainfall records used in the FEH come from a large and relatively comprehensive set of daily and sub-daily raingauges, including the more important national records computerised by the Met. Office. However, many rainfall records prior to 1961 are held only in manuscript form, principally at the National Meteorological Library and Archive, Bracknell. These can be particularly valuable in detailed studies of particular flood events. Other sources of rainfall data are discussed in Sections 6.3 and 6.4.

6.2 Flood peak data

The flood peak datasets used in the FEH research are supplied on the flood data CD-ROM accompanying Volume 3. These comprise annual maximum series for 1000 stations and peaks-over-threshold (POT) series for 890 stations. The annual maximum series have a typical end-date in the mid 1990s. The POT series are less up-to-date, with a typical end-date in the mid 1980s. There are, however, exceptions – notably in Scotland, Northern Ireland and the Northumbrian area of north-east England – where more recent POT flood data have been abstracted to a standard approximating that defined in the Flood Studies Report (see **3** 23). The University of Dundee has continued a tradition, started at St. Andrews, of university researchers leading the updating of Scottish flood series.

The major UK river gauging authorities are the Environment Agency (in England and Wales), the Scottish Environment Protection Agency, and the Northern Ireland Rivers Agency. General information about UK river gauging stations can be obtained from the National Water Archive at the Institute of Hydrology.

The WINFAP-FEH software package provides a framework within which the user can edit and extend the annual maximum and POT flood series published with the Handbook. Where the subject site is at, or close to, a gauging station, the flood series should be acquired or updated by obtaining peak flow data – or river level data and rating equations – from the relevant gauging authority. Ideally this will be fully co-operative, with the gauging authority giving local information and hydrometric guidance, and receiving a copy of any newly abstracted flood series. Regrettably, not all gauging authorities abstract annual maxima in water-year format (see **3** 23); this gives scope for confusion when series are updated.

The Volume 3 procedures for flood frequency estimation adopt a 'similar site' pooling scheme. This means that pooled analyses use flood series from catchments judged to be hydrologically similar to the subject site. Usually, this will include any flood records at, or close to, the subject site. However, in most cases, the pooled analysis will also include flood series from catchments that are (geographically) distant from the subject site.

This aspect has a profound impact for the way that datasets are organised to support the practical needs of those estimating design floods. Close co-operation with the area or regional office of the gauging authority will continue to be important to ensure that local and historical aspects of a particular flooding problem are fully understood. However, it will also be beneficial to gain access to updated flood series in other regions.

It is suggested that the resulting wide demand for updated flood series will precipitate a networked database of UK flood peak data, with updates compiled or vetted by the relevant gauging authority. Notwithstanding the importance of flood peak data, their abstraction and validation are time-consuming and require considerable attention to detail (see 3 23). It is therefore desirable that a networked database encourages effective use and expansion of holdings, while sustaining data quality standards.

The flood peak data are published here as flows, in accordance with the brief for the FEH research. Although a demanding task, there would be considerable merit in publishing both flood flows and flood levels, together with the level-flow relationships linking the two. Applications such as flood risk mapping (Chapter 9) call for a good appreciation of flow-depth relationships, and many historical flood data take the form of peak water levels rather than peak flows.

Flood peak datasets

The new or occasional user should seek guidance to ensure that they do not overlook important updates to national flood peak datasets.

6.3 Flood event data

Flood event data are sets of (usually) hourly rainfall and river flow data for specific floods. The acquisition and analysis of flood event data are described in Appendix A of Volume 4. This appendix also summarises the flood event data held at the Institute of Hydrology, both in tables and on the accompanying floppy disk.

River flow data are generally obtained from the gauging authority (see §6.2). Rainfall and climate data are held by the UK Met. Office, with major offices in Bracknell, Glasgow, and Belfast. Other sources of rainfall data include river gauging authorities, water supply utilities, and local authorities. Many organisations and individuals measure daily rainfalls, and some monitor rainfall at a finer temporal resolution or observe other climate variables. It can therefore be helpful to search relatively widely when seeking to reconstruct data for a particular extreme event (see 4 5). Weather radar data, co-ordinated by the Met. Office, are valuable in determining temporal and spatial patterns, and – when used carefully – in validating unusual rainfall observations.

6.4 Historical flood data

Historical floods are floods preceding the gauged period of record for which there is contemporary information, such as newspaper reports, or visual evidence, such as flood marks.

Historical information about floods is often given in earlier studies of a flooding problem. Various additional sources of information can be explored, including:

- Abstraction of heavy-rainfall dates and data from: long-term rainfall records (see §6.1); **British Rainfall** yearbooks; periodicals with a particular UK emphasis such as **Meteorological Magazine** (and its predecessor **Symons's Monthly Meteorological Magazine**), **Weather** and the less-formal-than-it-sounds **Journal of Meteorology**; and the **Climate Observers Link**;

- Searches of documents held in public libraries: local, district and regional;

- Inspection of newspaper records for specific dates when – judged from other evidence – floods may have occurred;

- Additional compilations and sources suggested by Potter (1978) and Jones *et al.* (1984).

Reports found often refer to earlier extreme events. A new source of information is the British Hydrological Society **Chronology of British Hydrological Events**, with the World Wide Web address: **http://www.dundee.ac.uk/geography/cbhe**.

Palæoflood data provide information about more extreme flood levels and/or velocities deduced from geomorphological evidence. Palæoflood studies comprise the sampling, dating and interpretation of old or ancient floodplain deposits. These are highly specialised tasks. There is a tradition of such studies in south-western parts of the USA (e.g. Baker, 1989). For those who believe in the concept of a Probable Maximum Flood (PMF), palæoflood data are seen as reinforcing the difficult interpolation between the 1000-year flood and the PMF (e.g. Ostenaa *et al.*, 1997). Otherwise, they can be used to complement or extrapolate a flood frequency analysis based on single-site, pooled and/or historical analyses. Their use in dam safety assessment is reviewed by USU and USBR (1999). Carling and Grodek (1994) explore several aspects of palæoflood data, and their interpretation, in UK conditions, including geomorphological evidence of the largest flood that has passed through a well-defined river section.

The general applicability of palæoflood methods in UK conditions is unclear. One limitation is that, in some districts, ploughing has disturbed the riparian zone in which palæoflood evidence might be expected to lie. However, the methods have the potential to inform the difficult problem of estimating very rare flood magnitudes, and their use should be considered in suitable cases.

Interlude: A sideways look at UK flood frequency estimation

Handbooks are sometimes criticised for being too prescriptive or for giving the impression that methods always work well. Despite praise from many quarters, the **Flood Studies Report** (NERC, 1975) was roundly condemned by one practical exponent of flood frequency estimation in the UK, who judged it a large step backwards (Bulman, 1984). Presumably Bulman believed that, in experienced hands, the methods he was already using were superior. Once clients insisted on use of the FSR, the scope for informed improvisation extended only to those methods, disallowing others. Might Bulman have been reacting against this exclusivity as much as the methods themselves? After all, a good recipe book, the right ingredients and a well-equipped kitchen do not guarantee a better meal.

This section of the Handbook tries to illustrate the dangers of simply adopting methods and clicking **calculate**. Familiarity with the FEH is no substitute for practical experience. The Interlude is deliberately unnumbered. It is intended to provoke thought and discussion: not to act as a source of authoritative reference. Nevertheless, each item is rooted in a real occurrence.

We're doing you a favour

Not many planning applications are submitted for building developments on isolated hill-tops. More typically, the proposal is to add to an established settlement, and the site is not far from a watercourse or river where flood risk is deemed a problem locally. Rather than acknowledging the basic truth – that incremental development increases runoff volumes incrementally – there is the cunning cry: "We're doing you a favour: the development will get the runoff away before the river flood peak arrives." If the regulator accepts this argument, there need be no balancing pond and no special expense.

Any minor (and rather speculative) benefit is strictly local. Allowing a development to discharge increased runoff-rates **will** aggravate flood risk lower down the river system. Even if, through accentuating the phasing of runoff from different parts of the catchment, flood peaks do not increase very much, overall runoff volumes certainly will. One of the less obvious effects of urbanisation is to widen the proportion of the year when floods occur. This is largely because urbanisation – through the extension of impervious and semi-pervious surfaces – reduces the beneficial buffering (i.e. absorbing) effect of seasonal soil moisture deficits. If floods occur more often, that represents an increase in flood frequency, at least at shorter return periods.

Environmental protection agencies in the UK are well attuned to taking a basin-wide view of flood risk, and to seeking to maintain the natural runoff regime where possible. Nevertheless, for a variety of reasons, it can still be difficult to ensure that planning consents deliver balancing ponds, or other drainage works, that meet basin-wide as well as local objectives.

We'll stick the balancing pond here

Techniques for dealing with increased runoff from development are now quite varied. Both larger-scale strategic solutions and smaller-scale source-control methods are considered, as well as balancing ponds. However, there was a period in which **balancing** the increased runoff became the reflex action to all drainage objections to development. The very word has a connotation of fairness that forestalls criticism. If the developer were to say instead "We'll mitigate the increased runoff by routing it through a reservoir with a controlled outlet that is designed to fail only occasionally", one might be more inclined to argue.

Many questions can be posed about a proposed balancing pond, including:

- Has the critical downstream site – where flooding will occur if balancing is not provided – been identified?

- Is the storage encouraging the separation or synchronisation of the natural and developed components of flood runoff to the critical site?

- What will the effects be – at the pond and at the critical site – when the design event is exceeded?

- Will the pond and adjacent works be onerous to maintain?

- Does the pond meet basin-wide as well as local objectives, or would a larger storage reservoir, placed strategically, be preferable?

It may not be cost-effective to challenge or prescribe the detailed design of every balancing pond. However, one question should always be asked:

- Will the pond occupy part of the natural floodplain?

Siting a balancing pond on a natural floodplain can be a form of double-counting. It presupposes that flood runoff from the development will not coincide with a period when the river is in flood. Particular circumspection is warranted before siting a balancing pond in an area that is flooded frequently (e.g. by spring tides) or for occasional extended periods (e.g. in the floodplain of a stream draining a highly permeable catchment).

Storing up problems

Given suitable local topography, diverting flood flows from constricted streams into a strategic flood storage reservoir can provide a deft solution. In essence, the strategy distils flooding problems on several adjacent streams into one decent-sized problem. The approach can work particularly well if the response characteristics of the diverted subcatchments are rather more rapid than those of the catchment chosen to house the storage reservoir. Gravity dictates that the receiving stream will be the lowest lying, where there may already be a wetland on which to focus a flood storage reservoir. Thus, it may just be a matter of raising an embankment, and providing a flow-control device to regulate discharges to within the carrying capacity of the channel downstream.

In one such scheme, design flood calculations correctly adopted a rainfall-runoff approach, and correctly applied a single design storm to the whole area contributing floodwater. Unfortunately, the design failed to allow for the **reservoir lag effect**: namely, that the attenuating effect of storage always makes a system sensitive to longer-duration events. As a generalisation, it seems that inspecting engineers never make this mistake yet flood storage scheme designers sometimes do. Perhaps the paradox is explained by the inspecting engineer's focus on reservoir safety, whereas the scheme designer may be preoccupied with flood alleviation.

In this instance, the designer compounded the mistake by concentrating resources still further. The scheme was varied to dispense with a troublesome pumping station that helped the downstream channel (between the reservoir and the estuary) to discharge at all states of the tide. The consequence was to halve the effective discharge capacity from the reservoir at a stroke, making the system sensitive to failure in exceptionally long-duration rainfall events. Having conceived such an imaginative solution, it is regrettable that, when the flawed scheme failed, the designer created a further diversion, by blaming the hydrologist.

Lengthy argument

In UK conditions, at least, it is fairly obvious that short wet periods occur more frequently than long wet periods. More generally, a short-duration rainfall of given rarity is more intense than a long-duration rainfall of the same rarity. Stating the very obvious, catchments that are typically sensitive to long-duration rainfalls are those that for one reason or another are rarely sensitive to short-duration rainfalls. Examples include large catchments, flat catchments, and catchments with a lot of storage.

Large catchments are usually insensitive to short-duration rainfalls because their response to rainfall is long drawn-out, with runoff from distant parts of the catchment taking a long time to reach the outlet. Unless runoff-producing conditions persist for many hours, the flood effect felt at the outlet will fall short of the catchment's full potential. This gives rise to the maxim that there is a critical duration of heavy rainfall to which a catchment is sensitive. The name ***time of concentration*** (correctly defined as "the time required for rain falling at the farthest point of the catchment to reach the outlet") might have lived on, had drainage engineers adopted an estimation method that reflected the time taken for runoff to reach the watercourse system, as well as travel times within the river system. A second reason why large catchments are generally insensitive to short-duration rainfalls is that short-duration storms tend to be spatially compact, and rarely extend over the whole drainage area.

Flat catchments may need substantial channels and pumping stations to drain them. Otherwise they will drain slowly and be typically sensitive to long-duration rainfalls.

A feature of catchments with large storage is that, in many rainfall events, quick response runoff only arrives from part of the catchment. On permeable catchments (i.e. with large natural storage), it will be that part of the catchment where soils are saturated: the so-called ***contributing area***. Where there are impounding reservoirs, runoff may only arrive from the unreservoired parts of the catchment. Both these cases present difficulty – in flood forecasting as well as in flood frequency estimation – because the catchment response is strongly influenced by the level of stored water in the soils, aquifer or reservoir, prior to the event. Although circumstances will be site-specific, barrages that are designed to retain water at all states of the tide are also likely to lengthen the typical duration of rainfall giving rise to (fluvial) flood risk.

Something to blame

Urbanisation can have a marked adverse effect on flood frequency if it extends over much of the drainage basin. Other land-use changes that are likely to have a

high impact include quarrying and opencast mining. Specific amelioration works are likely to be necessary in all these cases. Plantation-forestry drainage, and moorland drainage, can also have pronounced effects. A particular feature of forestry is that it typically occurs in units large enough to extend over much (or all) of smaller catchments. These are major land-use effects, and must be taken seriously. Sections 9.3 to 9.6 of Volume 4 provide a discussion, and point to some specific research results.

From time-to-time and place-to-place, less dramatic land-use changes are alleged to increase flood frequency. The list includes field under-drainage (i.e. subsurface drainage), ploughing, over-grazing, the removal of hedgerows and the filling of hollows. Several difficulties arise in trying to verify or discount effects. A typical scenario is that:

- A qualitative argument from first principles, suggests that, at the very local scale, the modification will increase runoff rates;

- The size of effect on flood frequency at the catchment-scale is uncertain, but is expected to be moderated by the patchwork nature of catchments (i.e. their mixed land covers and land uses);

- The effect at catchment-scale is difficult to monitor because of the natural variability of climate.

In general, the effect can be confirmed only by recourse to long-term paired-catchment experiments, in which the land use is modified on one catchment and unmodified on the other. Such experiments are expensive to mount and difficult to sustain unaltered over the required period. Three to five years of data may suffice to demonstrate the typical effect on catchment runoff, and five to ten years to assess the likely effect on the median annual flood. But it is rarely practical to sustain controlled experiments for the 25 to 50 years needed to detect the effect on extreme flood behaviour empirically. For this reason, studies of the impact of land-use change on flood frequency are more usually based on short-term plot studies (to understand the processes involved) and catchment modelling (to extrapolate to larger areas and more extreme events).

No less a practical difficulty can be that the person alleging the adverse land-use effect on flood frequency simply **knows** that the catchment-scale effect is large; this reduces the likelihood of constructive dialogue. Where long-term catchment experiments have been carried out, effects have seldom proved to be as strong or as straightforward as hypothesised (Rodda, 1976; Whitehead and Robinson, 1993).

Someone to blame

It is unclear whether the severe UK floods experienced in the 1990s have been notably aggravated by land-use (or climate) change. Counter-examples are easier to find: the Calderdale storm of 19 May 1989 would have had greater impact had part of the runoff not been detained or delayed by water-supply reservoirs.

Certainly, where developments have been allowed on floodplains, those land-use changes have increased the **impact** of flooding. So too have social changes: the separation of townhouses into flats, the carpeting of basements, and reduced tolerance when the river calls in unannounced. Lax planning has played a major part, and is summed up by the Borough Council that proposed and sanctioned a leisure centre with an occasional water sports facility well known to the river authority. On local government reorganisation, the council's new name was christened when the river made its first visit in 1974. The leisure centre was flooded twice more in 1979, and severely flooded in April 1998. On that occasion, the District Council admitted that the leisure centre had been built on the floodplain – on a site that was known to have flooded in 1947 – and coolly blamed its predecessor.

This example is symptomatic of the planning problem. In many cases, flood risk is accorded the attention it deserves only when a major event has occurred within the last 20 or so years. When the intended level of protection is against the 50 or 100-year event, it is inevitable that some communities will be caught out by the failure to review, and heed, contemporary accounts of past floods.

The view that there is **always** someone to blame is captured by the Chief Emergency Officer who volunteered in a discussion of flood risk: "There is no such thing as a natural disaster". One hopes that his department is lucky enough not to experience a 1000-year flood on any river, or a 100-year flood in a major community.

You call that a flood?

From a global perspective, flooding in the UK is small beer. There have been few dramatic incidents arising from landslide or debris dams, and their subsequent overtopping and failure. Also, communities at risk in the UK from large embanked rivers traversing low-lying land are smaller or less vulnerable than in, for example, the Netherlands, Bangladesh or China.

With many communities sited downstream of water-supply and amenity dams in Pennine and other steep-sided valleys, the UK potential for flood-induced catastrophe is, however, a significant one. Dam safety assessments seek to control the risk of dam-failure due to an overtopping flood, but cannot eliminate it. Landslides **do** occur on steeper slopes and less stable strata; the potential for exceptional occurrences is heightened following uncommonly wet periods. Severe drought can increase short-term flood risk on catchments where baked or cracked soils promote rapid runoff. Other fears are associated with the possible occurrence of exceptional convectional storms – both single and multi-cellular – or the freak ingress of a storm of tropical origin. No degree of sophistication in the type of statistical or rainfall-runoff approaches covered in this Handbook can explicitly allow for the unobserved. Other approaches must be considered to look at the potential effect of unobserved conditions such as dam failure or bridge collapse.

Many communities lie in river corridors, and many UK towns and cities are served by extensive flood defences. Most people and properties in vulnerable areas are defended. With some exceptions – e.g. those with a direct view of the river or the flood defence – most occupiers have little appreciation that defences can be overtopped in an extreme event. Paradoxically, flood alleviation presents an additional hazard: the hazard of unpreparedness when the defence is eventually overtopped. One hopes that emergency planners and reinsurers understand that large rivers – such as the Trent and Thames – present large flooding problems. They too have the same risk of experiencing a 100-year event as any other: a 0.01 probability in any year. The conditions giving rise to an exceptional flood on a large basin do not preclude the possibility of many basins being affected simultaneously, as occurred most notably in: November 1771 (north-east England, in particular), early 1883 (much of England), October 1903 (much of western

Britain) and March 1947 (south and east Britain). There was spatially extensive flooding in England and Wales also in 1852 and 1875, although different regions were affected in different months. More recent spatially extensive events include December 1979 (South Wales and south-west England) and April 1998 (central England and mid Wales). The scope for exceptional losses in a metropolis is illustrated by the high impact of the 10-11 December 1994 floods in and around Glasgow.

The throw of the dice

A town at the confluence of two rivers experiences no flood for many years, and then two extreme events occur in quick succession, both from tributary A. Another town experiences a succession of floods, each one larger than the preceding one. In such cases, it may prove difficult to convince those affected that it is a matter of chance, rather than a signal of land-use or climate change, or mismanagement of defences. In the older urban centres at least, contemporary records can be searched for long-forgotten floods and their impacts. A precedent is always helpful to public understanding of risk.

Rarely well done

Rainfall rarity estimates help to describe the exceptional characteristics of a flood-producing rainfall event (Jack, 1981). But, with few exceptions, it is wrong to assume that rainfall rarity ***determines*** flood rarity.

Four people died in the December 1979 floods in South Wales. Two were swept away as main rivers in the region reached danger levels, but two others drowned in their home near Merthyr Tydfil, as a result of flooding from a small steep catchment. During the event, a culvert under a disused mineral railway blocked, and some 20000 m^3 of water was inadvertently impounded behind the embankment, to a depth of about seven metres. The subsequent dam-burst flood overwhelmed the watercourse. Part of the flood wave was diverted down a railway cutting; the remainder shot down the watercourse, found a partial obstruction, and jetted into housing. In reaching a verdict of accidental death, the coroner determined that the deaths resulted from an exceptional storm, referring to a rainfall return-period estimate of 80 years (South Wales Echo, 19 March 1980). However, the storm did not include any intense short-duration rainfalls of the kind expected to be critical to flooding on a steep shallow-soiled 1.4 km^2 catchment. A later assessment (see Reed, 1987), using the method restated in **4 5**, indicated only a 5-year flood peak. Subsequently, those responsible for maintenance of the culvert settled a compensation claim, without admitting liability. There are perhaps three lessons from the episode:

- Unless account is taken of catchment sensitivities, an assessment of rainfall rarity can be a poor guide to flood rarity;

- If blockages occur (e.g. through landslides, debris, or poor maintenance), long-duration rainfall events present a particular hazard: even on quickly responding catchments;

- Even a reservoir or balancing pond smaller than 25000 m^3 – the lower limit to statutory inspections under the Reservoirs Act – can pose a threat to life, if stream channels are steep and people are close by.

A rarity assessment from rainfall data is of greater use where the storm event is exceptionally severe and highly localised (e.g. Calderdale, 19 May 1989; Llandudno,

11 June 1993). If the assessed return period is, say, longer than a thousand years, this will often be enough to suggest that the flood is too rare to be defended against cost-effectively.

A particularly troubling case is when an unexceptional rainfall event yields a flood of immense impact. This is possible on relatively permeable catchments, if the rainfall event occurs when the catchment is unusually ripe for flooding following a prolonged wet spell. It is characteristic of permeable catchments that, in lesser events, only part of the drainage area contributes to quick runoff. For a highly permeable catchment underlain by deep aquifers, the stream response to heavy rainfall is typically both slow and low. Flood behaviour on a moderately permeable catchment, underlain by an aquifer with less extensive storage potential, may be particularly difficult to discern, even when 20 years of flow data are available. A classic example is the Kenwyn at Truro which yielded not one but two large floods in 1988, from rainfall events that were not, in themselves, exceptionally rare (Acreman and Horrocks, 1990).

Outliers

A flood that is much higher than other recorded floods can be termed an **outlier**. However, this does not mean that the flood can be deleted from the record, as if it never happened.

Barnett and Lewis (1984) present almost 500 pages on the identification and treatment of outliers. Some of the writing is surprisingly discursive for a statistical text, though for good reason. Ferguson (1961) defines an outlier as an observation that is "surprisingly far away from the main group". Surprise is conditioned on the extremeness of the incident and on one's experience or expectation. Thus, when it comes to an outlier in flood data, the degree of surprise depends on how different the value is to other values in the series, and on the analyst's general experience of floods and flood data. Because different people have different experiences and expectations, it is unsurprising that the treatment of outliers can lead to strong emotion.

Barnett and Lewis suggested four possible treatments for outliers. They can be:

- **Rejected** as erroneous. This is appropriate if the outlier results from a mistaken reading but inappropriate if it is simply poorly measured;

- **Identified** as important. This treatment may be appropriate where a series includes several outliers. If these are held to be most relevant to the problem, the analyst concentrates on the outliers and pays less attention to the main (non-extreme) data;

- **Tolerated** within the analysis. Barnett and Lewis call this "accommodating" the outlier. This tactic assumes that the procedure is **robust against outliers**, i.e. that the analysis will not be seriously distorted by their presence;

- **Incorporated** into the analysis. In this case, the analysis defers to the outlier. The procedure is varied in a manner that is consistent with the outlier being not as extreme as implied by the standard analysis. As an example, a different distribution or fitting method might be specially adopted.

It is reprehensible that some analysts delete an outlier from a gauged record, with the quick comment that the event comes from a different population to that represented by other floods in the series. There is nothing wrong in asserting that

the outlier represents a different kind of flood; the bad practice lies in ignoring it. Those who simply disregard an inconvenient flood, muttering "outlier", should be chained to the river-bank.

In some parts of the world, it is possible to distinguish floods according to their origin: for example, distinguishing floods produced by tropical cyclones from those produced by other weather systems. The floods are segregated into two sets of extremes, each being analysed separately. The results of the two frequency analyses are then reassembled to provide a composite flood frequency curve. Although less convincing, this kind of two-component analysis can also be contemplated without prior segregation, if inspection suggests that there are ordinary extremes (forming a **normal series**) and exceptional extremes (forming an **outlier series**). Pegram and Adamson (1988) do this for 1-day rainfall extremes in southern Africa.

But it's an extraordinary flood

The argument is made that an extraordinary flood has occurred within the gauged period only by chance: surely, to accept it will lead to overestimation of the flood frequency curve? The view deserves respect where the analyst has gone to the trouble of demonstrating, by searching historical records, that the flood outstrips anything experienced in a period several times longer than that gauged. Nevertheless, the view can still be something of an over-reaction. It overlooks that flood frequency estimation procedures are designed to be robust against outliers.

Several developments help to make the FEH statistical flood frequency estimation procedure (Volume 3) relatively robust against outliers:

- Averaging data from many sites (i.e. pooled frequency analysis);
- Distribution fitting by L-moment methods;
- Less extravagant extrapolation of single-site analyses.

The recommendation to pool catchments according to hydrological similarity provides further security against an outlier having undue influence. Because catchments are no longer grouped regionally, the procedure is more robust against spatially extensive extreme events (see Reed and Stewart, 1991).

Missing outliers

Exceptional events are difficult to gauge. It is important to note that data archivers occasionally eliminate extreme events, or periods of record which include an extreme event, because of measurement uncertainty. It seemed good to hear (see May, 1985) that the use of weather radar data had helped the Met. Office to validate an isolated extreme raingauge reading. However, the unstated corollary was unsettling: the quality control system was judging isolated extreme values guilty until proven innocent. Despite very severe impacts in Calderdale, and geomorphological evidence of exceptional runoff rates in the worst-affected tributary, the Met. Office rejected the rainfall depth of 193.2 mm gauged at Walshaw Dean Lodge in the 19 May 1989 event: a decision challenged by Acreman and Collinge (1991). Though missing from the national database, the observation was included in the annual maximum rainfall dataset used in the FEH rainfall frequency analysis (Volume 2). Rainfall data are gathered and used for many purposes, and their effective archiving is dependent on considerable public investment. If this is to be strengthened, hydrologists and engineers need to report back their appreciation of the value of what is there, as well as regret at what is not.

Problems are not limited to rainfall data. The annual maximum flood series for a gauging station damaged by a flood may simply appear to be discontinued, or to have one or two values missing. During the FEH research, the annual maximum series for the Hebden Beck at Hebden (station 27002) was queried because the 2-year flood (*QMED*) estimated from flood data was very much lower than that expected from catchment descriptors (see **3** Additional Note 13.1). An explanation was found in the station description: much of the catchment is strongly karstic (i.e. limestone terrain with underground drainage). Such situations are relatively rare in the UK, and require special treatment. The station was therefore discarded from analysis, but not before a search of manuscript records unearthed an account (Pirt, 1975) of the exceptional flood of 13 August 1975, which severely damaged the gauging station. This had an estimated peak flow of 27 $m^3 s^{-1}$, more than seven times *QMED*. However, the report identified that the flood peak had been inflated by the bursting of an informal dam presented by an embanked access road across the karstic part of the catchment. In consequence, the annual maximum value for the 1974 water-year was formally judged unknown.

The data archiver has a difficult task, and may not deserve the flood analyst's opprobrium for excluding uncertain or irregular values. However, it is the analyst who will be criticised if the flood risk assessment proves to be a serious under-estimate. These examples illustrate the value of database structures that allow the storage and display of comments.

It's the software's fault

Inevitably, software packages – particularly those with a limited target market – will not provide the facilities that every user would wish. At the critical moment, the cry will be heard: "Why doesn't it even do this?" One user wished to incorporate a number of historical flood data into a frequency analysis of annual maximum floods: something that the particular package did not cater for. The user solved the problem by treating the record as a very long gauged series, entering a zero value whenever the annual maximum was unknown. This introduced a gross bias into the flood frequency estimation. The mistake would have been less easy to make if the package been designed to reject zero values. However, that might have caused another user to rail: a zero value can represent a true annual maximum on an arid, or very permeable, catchment. The rights and wrongs are immaterial; there may be good reason why the package does not provide the desired option, or it may have been designed too narrowly. Either way, it is the user's responsibility to understand the ***principles*** of the methods well enough to realise when extra clicking is not enough. Use of software may be necessary, but it is never compulsory; there is always the option to contract the flood frequency investigation to someone with greater expertise.

Minimising waste

Similar principles apply when recycling a model from an earlier study of a catchment. While it can be helpful to the client to build on previous work, the approach can sometimes be mistaken. A rainfall-runoff model calibrated for design use ***can*** (probably) be transformed into a flood forecasting model, but it will require expertise in both topics to be done dependably. Just because a catchment model is available, it should not necessarily be used. Apart from the possibility of misuse, recycling a model has the additional drawback of neglecting recent flood data; moreover, it diffuses responsibility for the results obtained.

Economical reporting

A "Parkinson's Law" of flood frequency estimation might be: "That the truth is never known, that what is known is rarely simple, and that what is known about what is known is seldom reported".

A flood occurs and a flood defence scheme is proposed; another flood occurs and the scheme is built; another flood occurs, the scheme fails and a higher defence is built; another flood occurs and the defence just holds. At each successive review, things become more problematic:

- After each newly observed flood is incorporated into the analysis, the perceived best estimate of the T-year flood increases;
- As each extreme flood occurs, a new consultant is appointed.

If investigation reveals that an important mistake was made, will its divulgence:

- Contribute to public understanding of flood risk?
- Lead to litigation?

Flood frequency estimation is such an uncertain business that the reviewer is only likely to condemn the grossest of errors. A more likely outcome will be to pronounce that:

- Some minor mistakes were made;
- The hydrology (a euphemism for the *flood frequency estimate*) has changed;
- Approval is being sought to construct a higher defence.

Unfortunately, there is a dreadful consequence. Reports will blur what is known or suspected. One or two floods down the line, those asked to investigate will find it all very confusing. Flood frequency estimation is difficult enough without having to cope with economical reports.

Taking centre stage

If there is a current trend in UK flood hydrology, it is perhaps that meteorology, hydrology and hydraulics have stopped drifting apart. It is an exciting challenge to draw them together in important applications such as flood warning and flood risk mapping. Let us hope that neither scientific excellence nor operational pragmatism is squeezed in the process.

It is widely recognised that pivotal factors in flood frequency estimation are the length of available record, the extent to which it is up-to-date, and the quality of flood flow measurement. Greater attention needs to be paid to measuring, validating and updating flood flows, and ways found to apply corrections retrospectively. Concern often centres on improving stage-discharge ratings: the formulae by which observed water levels are transformed to river flows. Customarily, these *flood ratings* are refined by direct gauging of flow velocities during floods. Hydraulic modelling of rivers and floodplains continues to advance, with greater use of computational rather than physical (i.e. scaled) models. Hydraulic theory, whether or not encapsulated within computational models, can provide useful insight into the hydraulic behaviour of gauging stations, and guide the extrapolation of rating curves beyond their limits. However, hydraulic models, like other models, need to be calibrated by reference to gauged data and experience. Experience derives from past studies, and, ultimately, from past gauged data. Matching an observed water surface profile down a river reach may be a good test of a hydraulic model, but it should not be seen as a substitute for measuring flood flows.

We can't afford more than half a day

Flood frequency estimation is quite a complicated subject, with few clear-cut answers. If there is good basic information to hand, half a day might just be adequate for a preliminary assessment. But, if the flood frequency estimate is to form the basis of an important decision, anything from five to 50 days will be more appropriate. The flood frequency estimate is usually instrumental in sizing a flood defence scheme and in assessing cost-effectiveness. Unless it is acceptable to the client and regulator to adopt a highly cautious design, the quality of the flood frequency estimate will largely determine the quality of the design decision. In this litigious age, it may be as important to be able to demonstrate that an assessment has been carried out systematically – by trained personnel, without corner-cutting – than for the estimate, with the benefit of hindsight, to have proven good. However great the cost of a thorough flood frequency appraisal, it is likely to be more affordable than half a day in court.

Chapter 7   Climate change

7.1   Background

There is evidence to suggest that human activity is influencing the world's climate. The chief agent is thought to be increased emissions of greenhouse gases, in particular carbon dioxide. The long time-scales governing the accumulation of greenhouse gases in the atmosphere, and the response of the global climate system to these accumulations, suggest that important aspects of human-induced climate change are effectively irreversible. In the words of the Working Group to the Second Assessment Report of the Intergovernmental Panel on Climate Change (Houghton *et al.*, 1996): ***The balance of evidence suggests a discernible human influence on global climate***.

Modelling global climate change is difficult and subjective, and both the techniques used and results obtained provoke controversy. Model-based projections of the effect of greenhouse gas emissions on global surface temperatures are, however, supported by observations that the global climate has warmed since the late 19th century (see Figure 7.1).

Global sea level has risen by between 10 and 25 cm over the past 100 years, and much of the rise is thought to be attributable to the increase in global mean temperature. This justifies Government advice (e.g. MAFF, 1993) to allow for continuing sea-level rise in coastal flood defence design. Based on the Hadley Centre climate model HadCM2 (see §7.2), Hulme and Jenkins (1998) suggest that, by the 2050s, mean sea levels around the UK will be 20 to 28 cm higher than in 1961-1990.

Implications of global warming for fluvial flooding are, in contrast, much more speculative. Hulme and Jenkins (1998) suggest that UK mean annual rainfall will be about 5% higher by the 2050s. However, this is but one of a range of

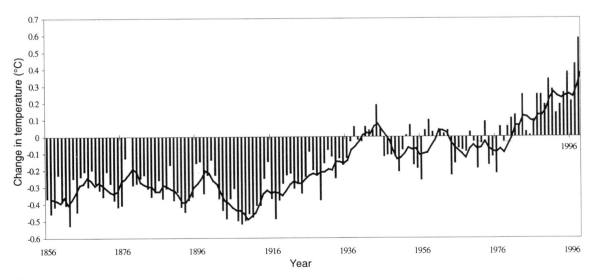

Figure 7.1 *Global mean annual temperatures for 1856 to 1998, expressed as a departure from the 1961-1990 mean, and the 5-year running mean of these departures (data courtesy of the Hadley Centre for Climate Prediction, the Met. Office)*

projections, some of which indicate much larger increases. The climate models suggest that winter (December to February) rainfalls will increase much more than annual totals, and that summer (June to August) rainfalls will decrease in south-east Britain. These projections in seasonal rainfall are relatively uncertain, and those of changes in storm depths and storm frequencies are highly uncertain. Box 7.1 offers a more detailed interpretation of the effect of global warming on UK rainfall regimes.

Box 7.1   An interpretation of global warming effects on UK rainfall regimes, based on Tabony (1999, pers. comm.)

The direct effect of global warming is to increase temperature and, all other things being equal, to increase rainfall and evaporation. This effect arises because an increase in temperature of 10°C is accompanied by a doubling in the amount of water vapour that the atmosphere can hold.

The indirect effect of global warming is to change patterns of atmospheric circulation. Computational model studies indicate that the mid-latitude weather belts will move poleward, and that the prevailing south-westerly winds between them will become even more dominant. In the vicinity of the UK, this means that Scotland and Northern Ireland will experience an increase in the frequency of south-westerly winds, while there will be a greater anticyclonic influence over south-east England. An outcome of this will be that annual rainfall totals will increase over western Scotland, with a possible decrease over south-east England. Superimposed on these changes will be an increase in the proportion of rain that falls in the winter half-year. The combined effect will lead to wetter winters in western Scotland and drier summers in south-east England.

These direct and indirect effects of global warming suggest an intensification of the hydrological cycle, with an increased risk of winter floods and a greater propensity for summer drought.

The change in weather patterns means that there is potential for an increase in the severity of convective storms over much of England. However, with little or no increase in total summer rainfall, the picture is one of any increase in severity being restricted to rare events. This is consistent with the frequency of convective storms being suppressed by high pressure.

A second difficulty in understanding the implications of global change is that rainfall regimes in the UK are naturally highly variable. An underlying trend has therefore to be strong and coherent – applying systematically to the particular variable over a wide region – if it is to be detected with confidence (§7.3). In the case of detecting trend in extreme rainfalls, there will be a greater chance of registering an effect if it applies over a range of durations.

A final difficulty is that the factors giving rise to flood occurrence are complex and non-uniform across catchments. Three examples hint at the variety:

- Some catchments in northern Britain are susceptible to flooding from rain and snowmelt, either separately or in conjunction. The projected rise in mean temperatures suggests that large snow-packs may accumulate rather less frequently, reducing the risk of snowmelt flooding in these catchments.

- Intense convectional storms are responsible for much of the flood risk on small urbanised catchments in lowland Britain. If global climate change leads to less frequent but more intense thunderstorms, this will increase the steepness of the flood frequency curves on these catchments.

- On many (essentially) rural catchments, extensive soil moisture deficits in summer and autumn play an important role in moderating flood frequency, particularly in drier and warmer parts of lowland Britain. Because winter is the main UK flood risk season, increased winter rainfall would be expected to increase flood magnitudes. However, this could be partly offset by there being somewhat fewer floods, as the flood risk season is compressed by more persistent soil moisture deficits.

A complication when anticipating climate change impacts is that not all of the UK experiences the same climate. There are important maritime, continental and latitudinal effects, with particularly pronounced differences between north-west Scotland and south-east England. Black (1996) speculates that climate change may be responsible for increased flood frequencies in western Scotland since 1988.

7.2 Climate change impact assessment

Knowledge of climate change impacts on rainfall and fluvial flood frequency will undoubtedly advance during the lifetime of the Handbook. As a guide to interpreting new findings, some of the language and methods of climate change impact assessment are briefly introduced.

Models

The main approach to assessing climate change impacts is through **modelling**. Global climate modelling is mainly carried out in specialised climate research centres. The leading UK group is focused on the DETR/Met. Office Hadley Centre for Climate Prediction. The Hadley Centre develops **global climate models** (GCMs), from which projections of global climate change can be made. These models are also known as **general circulation models**, with the same abbreviation. There are different generations of models, which incorporate new or revised elements. HadCM2 denotes the Hadley Centre climate model developed in the mid 1990s. The next-generation model is HadCM3.

Many of the developments seek to improve the representation of **feedback** within the global climate system. Feedback occurs when the effect of a particular change is accentuated or moderated by some consequential effect. For example, a change in global surface temperature affects the prevalence of ice and snow-covered surfaces. These surfaces reflect solar radiation more strongly, being said to have a high **albedo**. If global warming leads to reduced snow-cover, which, in turn, leads to lower outgoing radiation, the warming is likely to be further enhanced; this is an example of **positive feedback**. Feedback can also arise from changes in terrestrial ecosystems – notably, vegetation and agricultural practice – consequent upon climate change.

Ocean currents play an important role in transporting heat around the globe. The most highly developed climate models are atmospheric and oceanic

GCMs. Sometimes, models of the oceanic and atmospheric circulations are developed separately, and then combined. The upshot is a **coupled** GCM.

Scenarios

Certain assumptions or hypotheses are needed when using a global climate model to project climate change. Some of the assumptions relate to how a particular process is represented within the GCM, while others relate to projections of anthropogenic change. For example, a run of a GCM will make particular assumptions about greenhouse gas and aerosol (i.e. microscopic airborne particle) emission rates over the period of projection: typically, the next 50 to 100 years. This means that the climate impact modeller is presented with several sets of projections. Each is a separate realisation of how the climate will evolve. These are generally referred to as climate change **scenarios**. Sometimes several projections are made using a particular GCM but a key assumption is varied to explore the sensitivity of projections to the particular assumption.

It is impractical to consider all possible scenarios, in which all combinations of assumptions are explored. Thus, the climate impact modeller will generally use a relatively small number of semi-standard scenarios. In the UK, these are currently disseminated from the Hadley Centre via the LINK project at the Climatic Research Unit at the University of East Anglia. Thus, to an extent, climate change research divides into two main activities: (i) modelling the global climate and making projections, and (ii) assessing the impact of the projected climate change. Nevertheless, much effort is being given to integration, to ensure that feedback effects are better represented.

Impacts

Climate change impacts are potentially of huge significance, and research is undertaken by many organisations. The more advanced appraisals are generally based on modelling. For example, Reynard *et al.* (1998) simulate river flows for the Severn and Trent using a catchment model operating at a daily time-step. Each climate change scenario leads to a different generated flow series. These are subsequently analysed as if they were gauged records. Given that river flows are simulated continuously, it is possible to adopt a peaks-over-threshold (POT) approach to flood frequency analysis. The impact of climate change on flood frequency is then inferred by comparing the flood frequency curve resulting from the particular scenario with that for a **baseline** condition. Often, a period drawn from the observational record will be used as the baseline, e.g. the 1961-1990 standard period. In other cases, the baseline will itself be a scenario, e.g. based on no change in greenhouse gas emissions.

A particular challenge in global climate modelling is to infer changes at the local or district level from climate changes projected at the regional or national level. This is sometimes referred to as the **downscaling problem**. Wilby *et al.* (1998) consider several approaches. One possibility is to use atmospheric circulation indices (e.g. Lamb, 1972) as an intermediary variable, as considered by Goodess and Palutikof (1998). A goal might be to establish a link between the frequency distribution of extreme rainfalls (locally) and the frequency of particular airflow circulation patterns (regionally).

Simpler approaches to assessing climate change impacts are possible, but are generally considered much less satisfactory. One is the **spatial analogue** technique, in which an analogy is drawn between the projected climate of the region of interest (e.g. southern England) and the current climate of another region (e.g. southern France). Climate data are then transferred from the analogue region to the subject region. A particular difficulty is the need to identify a region that is in other respects (e.g. topography, closeness to oceans) similar to the subject region, and for which relevant data are available. Another simple approach is the *temporal analogue* method. This works by selecting warm and cool periods from the long time-span for which rainfall (or river flow) data are available. Typically, the difference in mean temperature between the warm and cool periods will be of the order of 1 or 2 °C. Rainfall frequency (or flood frequency) is examined separately for the warm and cool periods, and a comparison made. It is assumed that the difference in behaviour between the two periods is indicative of the difference that might be expected due to a rise in mean temperature consequent upon global warming. This approach has many limitations, including the requirement for very long records, and the difficulty of selecting contrasting periods that are individually long enough to allow a frequency analysis of extremes. However, the chief weakness is the assumption itself. Many climatologists reject these analogue methods.

7.3   Detecting climate change impacts

It is sometimes argued that a climate change impact cannot be very serious if it is not evident in data records. This view is complacent. There are two main reasons why it is difficult to detect underlying trends in flood peaks: the large natural variability of climate, and interference from other effects (notably, changes in land use and measurement practice).

Climatic variability

The first obstruction to detecting trend is the large variability of climate on all time-scales. Several types of variation can be distinguished. Yevjevich (1991) notes four categories of temporal behaviour: tendency, intermittency, periodicity and stochasticity. This is broadly the classification used here, distinguishing:

- Progressive change or *trend*;
- Abrupt change or *step change*;
- Quasi-periodic (i.e. cyclical) variation;
- Quasi-random variation.

It is suggested that this list places the four types of variation in their order of importance in terms of detecting climate change impacts (and land-use change impacts) and of disrupting flood frequency estimates. When the FEH refers to *non-stationarity* it is primarily referring to trend and step-change effects. The prefix "quasi" pays deference to chaos theory. Computational experiments demonstrate that both behaviour that appears regular and behaviour that appears random can have a complex deterministic origin.

There is evidence of periodic behaviour in some climate variables (e.g. Currie, 1987). However, there is controversy about both their origin and their practical significance. One view is that the behaviour reflects solar disturbances, with effects transported to the earth's atmosphere by the *solar wind*: solar particle streams accompanied by strong magnetic fields emanating from the sun (Lamb, 1972). There is the suspicion that some detected cyclic behaviour may be spurious, arising as an artefact of the relatively short records available. Burroughs (1992) suggests that only an 18 to 20-year cycle – possibly corresponding to the 18.6-year luni-solar cycle in gravitational forces – is sufficiently prevalent in climate data to suggest an important effect.

There is no evidence yet to suggest that cyclicity is important in understanding short-duration rainfall extremes or river flooding in the UK, beyond the general observation that there are **flood-rich** and **flood-poor** periods (Grew and Werritty, 1995). Such periods can extend over several years or even a decade. When summarising flood behaviour in Scotland, Grew and Werritty suggest that the late 1960s and early 1970s were flood-poor, with a flood-rich period beginning in the mid 1980s. Crooks (1994) examines peak flood levels along the Thames for the period 1890-1990, noting a preponderance of high peaks in the first half of the record, i.e. before 1940.

Contaminating effects

The second obstruction to detecting climate-change induced effects is that the flood series presented for analysis may be contaminated by other changes: for example, in land use, water use, or measurement practice. Land-use change such as urbanisation or forestry is likely to lead to progressive change in flood behaviour. Changes attributable to reservoir construction, drainage diversion, or use of a different flood rating are likely to be abrupt.

Methods and results

The analysis of trend and variation in flood data is explored in Volume 3. Methods are presented for testing for trend and step change (**3** 21.2), with results summarised for 1000 UK flood series (**3** 21.3 and 21.4). A national perspective is also drawn (**3** 21.5), based on Robson *et al.* (1998). While clear evidence is found of major climatic fluctuations (i.e. flood-rich and flood-poor periods), no proof is found that climate change is affecting UK flood behaviour. However, for the reasons introduced above, this does not mean that such effects are not occurring. The FEH recommends that estimates of the 2-year flood, *QMED*, derived from short records should be adjusted for climatic variation by reference to long-term records from nearby catchments, ideally from nearby catchments that are hydrologically similar (see **3** 20).

These findings can be considered provisional. They are conditioned as much by the data analysed as by the methods used. Understanding would be strengthened by the analysis of updated flood peak datasets, by more specific (e.g. regional) studies, and by an auxiliary analysis of trend and variation in rainfall depths. The latter would be assisted by wider access to long-term computerised records of UK rainfall.

Chapter 8   Development-control applications

8.1   Introduction

Extensive urbanisation has a marked effect on catchment flood behaviour (Packman, 1980; Hall, 1984). The FEH discusses this in the context of both statistical flood frequency estimation (see **3** 18) and the FSR rainfall-runoff method (see especially **4** 9.3). In their development-control function, planning authorities need to be satisfied that a development neither lies in a flood-prone area nor will increase flood frequency locally. In union with environmental protection agencies, they also need to ensure that, in the longer term, progressive development does not aggravate flood risk at the river basin scale; the general aim is to seek to alter the natural runoff regime as little as possible. Other land-use change, such as quarrying, agricultural drainage or deforestation, may also influence flood frequency (see **4** 9.4 to 9.6). However, this chapter is specifically concerned with problems arising from urban expansion.

8.2   Judging the extent of catchment urbanisation

The flood frequency estimation procedures presented in Volumes 3 and 4 are calibrated on flood data from 873 and 204 catchments respectively. Table 8.1 indicates the broad range of catchment types used, and summarises the FEH terminology for different degrees of catchment urbanisation.

Table 8.1   Numbers of catchments used in calibration of FEH methods: arranged according to the degree of urbanisation

Degree of catchment urbanisation	Range of URBEXT	No. of catchments used	
		QMED modelling (Volume 3)	Tp modelling (Volume 4)
Essentially rural	0.000 – 0.025	687	146
Slightly urbanised	0.025 – 0.050	71	25
Moderately urbanised	0.050 – 0.125	81	18
Heavily urbanised	0.125 – 0.250	20	12
Very heavily urbanised	0.250 – 0.500	14	3
Extremely heavily urbanised	0.500 – 1.000	0	0

The table refers to the catchment descriptor *URBEXT*. This is the principal FEH index of urbanisation, and represents the fractional urban extent judged from digital maps of land cover at 50-metre intervals. These are adapted from the Institute of Terrestrial Ecology (ITE) land-cover map, based on satellite imagery (see **5** 6). It should be noted that:

- Volume 5 presents values of *URBEXT* for gauged catchments studied in the FEH;

- The accompanying FEH CD-ROM presents *URBEXT* values for all UK catchments which drain an area of 0.5 km² or greater;

- The *URBEXT* values indicate urban extent in about 1990;

- The FEH CD-ROM software provides an image of catchment development, distinguishing 50-metre grid-squares that are rural, suburban and urban. The suburban category is an intermediate classification, used to indicate a grid-square that is partially covered by urban-like surfaces;

- The ITE land-cover map does not extend to Northern Ireland; *URBEXT* values there have been estimated from the less detailed CORINE classification. These *URBEXT* values are less reliable, and reference to OSNI 1:50000 maps is recommended (see **5** 6).

- ITE is developing an updated land-cover map, due to be published in 2000/2001.

In catchments that have undergone notable urban development since 1990, values of *URBEXT* can be updated in any of three ways:

- Apply local knowledge to judge the factor by which catchment urbanisation has expanded beyond that shown on the FEH CD-ROM image;

- Apply, and extrapolate, a British-average model of urban expansion (see **5** 6);

- Apply an adjustment judged by comparing OS maps of 1990 and current vintage.

In catchments that are to undergo further development, it is necessary to anticipate the urban expansion that is relevant to the flood risk assessment or scheme design. In projecting the expected increase in *URBEXT*, account can be taken of the nature of development by comparison with how a known development of similar character has been mapped.

8.3 *Discussion of methods*

The statistical flood frequency estimation procedure (Volume 3) is applicable to rural catchments and, with the appropriate urban adjustments, to urbanised catchments. The urban adjustments are calibrated directly on flood peak data for 115 catchments: those in the moderately urbanised, heavily urbanised and very heavily urbanised categories (see Table 8.1). In consequence, the method provides an estimate of flood frequency for urbanised catchments that have had a ***typical*** degree of flood amelioration works. It is essential to recognise that the urban adjustment method represents only the ***net*** effect of urbanisation, i.e. that element which drainage works have not ameliorated. Because allowances for catchment urbanisation are more fully integrated into the method, Section 5.7 suggests that with caution the rainfall-runoff method (Volume 4) can be used to assess the incremental effect of development.

Experimental studies (e.g. Hollis, 1974; Knight, 1979; Walling, 1979; Packman, 1980) indicate that the gross effect of urbanisation is generally very marked at the small-catchment scale typical of many development-control applications. However, these studies have not been fully generalised and it remains necessary to apply engineering judgement to assess the expected gross effect of catchment urbanisation on flood runoff. A pragmatic approach will be to sustain and strengthen current practice to ameliorate flood runoff effects, both through flood storage reservoirs and balancing ponds, and by greater use of source-control methods (Anon, 1993; SEPA/EA, 1997) including infiltration drainage (Bettess, 1996).

Section 12.6 advocates research on the flood runoff effects of developments on greenfield sites. While urbanised catchments are present in the FEH flood peak dataset (see Table 8.1), these are typically much larger than, and of a different character to, the drainage areas pertinent to individual development-control applications. The FEH CD-ROM provides digital catchment data to allow flood frequency estimation for any site in mainland UK (see §2.4.2) that drains an area of 0.5 km² or greater. This lower limit reflects the resolution of the basic digital data, and means that the Handbook methods cannot be readily applied to flood design for catchments smaller than 0.5 km² (i.e. 50 hectares).

Any valley bottom is a potential flood route that should not be obstructed by housing. Particular care is advised when designing drainage systems for developments on highly permeable catchments that, in their natural condition, lack any stream network. Unless there are water quality implications, soakaway systems may present an attractive option. However, the possibility should be borne in mind that runoff from a high-intensity storm could occur at a time when groundwater levels are high due to long-term or seasonal wetness, or when the soakaway system is draining from an earlier storm. Such situations present a kind of joint probability problem (see Appendix B). Rather than attempting a formal solution, it may be necessary to exercise engineering judgement, perhaps making what is perceived to be a fairly cautious assumption. In the longer term, the difficulty may be sidestepped by appropriate developments to the continuous simulation approach to flood frequency estimation (see §9.6).

Chapter 9   Flood risk mapping

9.1   Requirement

The classic problem addressed by the Handbook is to estimate flood frequency for a specific site. The result is usually an estimate of the peak flow that has a specified probability of exceedance, such as an annual exceedance probability of 0.01. The preferred method depends largely on the available data and the target return period (see Chapter 5).

In flood risk mapping, the requirement is to identify areas at risk of inundation. The requirement is met by estimating flood flows at many sites along the river system, interpreting the flows in terms of resultant water levels, and identifying riparian areas that will flood in consequence.

There is a strong demand for flood risk mapping from a range of stakeholders, including agencies responsible for flood defence and flood warning, development planners, insurers and solicitors. Flood risk mapping is at its most contentious when carried into *red-lining*: i.e. when property is marked as being at such high risk as to be uninsurable at normal premiums. The practice can affect property values and ease of sale.

Flood risk mapping calls for flood frequency to be estimated for many sites, each estimation providing a footprint of flood risk on the local landscape. The basin-wide flood risk map is then constructed by merging the results of the individual analyses.

Box 9.1 Constructing a basin-wide map of flood risk

The required map of areas at risk is constructed by merging results from individual assessments for many sites down the river system. For example, a basin-wide map of the 100-year flood risk zone is obtained by drawing an envelope around areas shown to be suffering an annual flooding risk of 0.01 in specific assessments.

9.2   Indicative maps of flood risk and floodplain extent

IH Report 130 (Morris and Flavin, 1996) presents an indicative flood risk map of England and Wales. The map is *indicative* (rather then definitive) in the sense that it is highly generalised. The hydrological content is a 3-variable model of the 100-year water level, based on drainage area ($AREA$), average annual rainfall ($SAAR_{4170}$) and the 5-class FSR index of *winter rainfall acceptance potential* ($SOIL$). The model was calibrated using flood data from 34 catchments (Naden and McCartney, 1991). Its simple form is well suited to automated application using catchment data based on the IH digital terrain model. This allowed Morris and Flavin to present a first general solution to flood risk mapping, and an extension to Scotland is in preparation. However, their method does not adjust the modelled 100-year water levels by reference to local flood data.

The IH Report 130 map is one ingredient of the Environment Agency's 1999 map of Indicative Floodplain Extent. This hybrid map combines historical, modelled and IH Report 130 estimates of areas that have an annual (fluvial) flood risk of 0.01 or greater. The EA map also shows areas having an annual tidal flood risk of 0.005 or greater. In general, the indicative maps do not take account of flood defences, and the probabilities quoted should be considered purely nominal.

Volume 3 of the FEH presents a comprehensive approach to peak flow estimation at any site, calibrated against flood data from a thousand catchments. Relatively sophisticated variants of the method are capable of full automation. Thus, there is scope to develop an advanced automated method of flood risk mapping (see §9.5).

9.3 A flood risk myth

There is no such thing as a basin-wide 100-year flood event. An actual flood event will be more severe at some locations than others, with river confluences reinforcing or diluting event rarity. The effect at each confluence depends mainly on whether both tributaries have experienced the particular storm, and the extent to which their catchments are hydrologically similar.

Different sites have different sensitivities. A design flood assessment attempts to provide a best estimate of the long-term flood risk, and must reflect these different sensitivities. Thus, it is impractical to construct a design event that will yield a flood of fixed rarity at all sites within a river basin (see Example 9.1). Any attempt to estimate the *T*-year flood condition throughout a river system by hydrological and hydraulic modelling of **one** design event should be shunned.

Example: 9.1 Urbanisation and flood seasonality

A heavily urbanised headwater catchment is generally sensitive to short-duration heavy rainfalls, which are more prevalent in summer (Fig. 9.1a). Flood risk at a site further down the river system (Fig. 9.1b) – where the urban influence has been diluted by tributaries – is likely to be sensitive to longer-duration rainfalls occurring in winter, when the catchment is already wet. Extreme floods at the two sites are clearly sensitive to different conditions. Any attempt to combine the two conditions within a single design event is likely to lead to unreliable results.

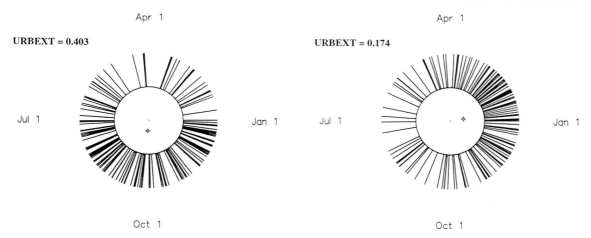

Figure 9.1 *Flood seasonality on the River Tame, east of Birmingham: (a) heavily urbanised headwater catchment, (b) mixed land-use catchment*

9.4   A workable approach

A typical approach to mapping flood risk in a particular basin is to combine the FSR rainfall-runoff method (Volume 4) – applied on a subcatchment basis – with a hydraulic model of the main river system. For reasons explained above, flood frequency estimates must be undertaken for a series of subject sites. Sites should be chosen above and below each major confluence. This extends the computational requirement very significantly (see Box 9.2).

Box 9.2   Overview of flood risk mapping by a design event method

Consider a trial site that lies part way down the river system for which flood risk is to be mapped. The rainfall-runoff approach (**4** 9.2.2) constructs a design storm that is relevant to the whole catchment draining to the trial site. For modelling purposes, the storm is applied separately to major tributaries within the catchment. The division into subcatchments is sensibly made to coincide with any gauging stations, to give scope to refine the rainfall-runoff model parameters by flood event analysis (Table 5.4) or – less directly – by statistical frequency analysis (**3** 10.2). The tributary hydrographs synthesised by rainfall-runoff modelling are then combined with that part of the hydraulic model representing the river system above (and just below) the trial site. The footprint of inundation is noted, and the whole process repeated for further trial sites.

Choosing trial sites above and below major confluences caters for river sections where backwater effects are important. The required basin-wide flood risk map is constructed by merging the flood footprints from the various trials. The area at risk is judged to be either the envelope of all the trial footprints, or an envelope drawn to respect the footprint from each trial locally.

The hydraulician can provide a unique computational model of the river system, which can be considered *the* model until new survey data or calibration data arrive. However, it is much more difficult to document the flood estimates that underpin a *T*-year flood risk map for the basin. Information to be recorded includes: design storms, local data, flows, water levels and inundated areas. With such complications, clarity in reporting is difficult to achieve, leaving scope for errors to pass undetected.

9.5   Automated flood risk mapping

Because its flood estimation procedures are capable of full automation, the FEH offers an important advance towards comprehensive flood risk mapping. The Handbook deals principally with flood flows. Hydraulic approximations are needed to convert the *T*-year flood flow into a water level. Then terrain data are required to spread the excess depth (above bankfull height) across the landscape so that flood risk areas can be mapped. There are several practical problems to be overcome: including that of incorporating information about the location and height of existing flood defences, so that protected and vulnerable areas can be distinguished. To keep the approach manageable, it is probably necessary to assume that the envelope of inundated areas – each inferred locally from the estimated *T*-year flood peak in that reach – yields an acceptable estimate of the required *T*-year flood risk area.

9.6   *Whole catchment modelling*

The development of a framework within which hydrological, hydraulic and various impact models can be integrated to provide **whole catchment modelling** is of considerable importance. The approach (Naden *et al.*, 1997) has particular relevance to estimating the likely impact of land-use and/or climate change on flood risk. Whole catchment modelling recognises that decisions taken in respect of one site have implications for sites downstream. There is also scope for the approach to meet multiple objectives; for example, a comprehensive model developed for planning strategic flood defences within a river basin may have application in water resource or water quality planning.

Several points should be kept in mind. First, the approach requires **continuous simulation** of runoff, which is hungry for detailed rainfall and runoff data (for model calibration) and for long-term rainfall records or generated rainfall series (to allow inferences to be made about extreme events). Second, because everything is modelled, it is possible for the risk assessment to be based on an extreme value analysis of the variable of direct interest, such as water level at a specific location. This feature of whole catchment modelling is potentially very helpful in avoiding both the sweeping assumptions of design event methods and the complications of joint probability problems (see Appendix B), provided that the relevant processes and their interactions can be modelled reliably.

At the time of writing, the continuous simulation approach to flood frequency estimation (e.g. Calver and Lamb, 1996) remains somewhat experimental. One quandary to be resolved is how the approach can best exploit conventional flood frequency analyses of long-term gauged records.

Chapter 10   Flood frequency estimation for public safety

10.1 Impounding reservoirs

Impounding reservoirs present a latent threat to public safety. Factors aggravating this in the UK are the prevalence of old earthen dams sited above the communities they were built to serve, and a lack of public awareness of the hazard. Factors offsetting this are the strong lead set by institutions, not least the formulation and sustenance of procedures for reservoir supervision and inspection (including ICE, 1996b), and the relatively mild meteorological and geophysical regimes experienced in the UK.

Flood frequency estimation in support of dam safety is, nevertheless, problematic. The estimation of design floods that have a very low probability of exceedance, e.g. an annual exceedance probability of 10^{-4}, relies on an act of faith. There are too few data to allow a purely empirical approach, and a model-based approach – whether statistical or rainfall-runoff – has to assume that the chosen model is applicable *in extrema*. It is tempting to seek solace in the concept of a **probable maximum flood** (PMF). However, a procedure for PMF estimation can be as much a product of the hydrologist's fertile imagination (about what unfavourable conditions might conceivably concur) as a product of physical reasoning. The consequential requirement for an estimate of **probable maximum precipitation** places a similar burden on the meteorologist.

These difficult circumstances encourage the adoption of fairly regimented methods for estimating design floods in dam safety assessment. Faced with inadequate information, it seems sensible to follow a standard method and to eschew any special adjustment that might inadvertently lead to underestimation. Conservatism is normally to be avoided in flood frequency estimation for fear of distorting benefit-cost ratios. However, economic factors are less dominant when public safety is at stake. There is an understandable reluctance to apply criteria for incorporating local evidence (e.g. from gauged or historical flood data) even-handedly. Where data transfers support a higher flood estimate, they will be heeded; where they suggest a lower estimate, they will be ignored. This practice has much to commend it. However, it would be disappointing if those recognising the bias interpreted it as a discouragement to gather and analyse local data. The inspecting engineer appointed under the Reservoirs Act is able to specify data to be gathered in support of safety assessments. These need not be restricted to measurements at the dam.

Rainfall-runoff method

Recommended practice in UK dam safety assessment is to synthesise the extreme flood from an estimate of extreme rainfall, using the FSR rainfall-runoff method (see **4 8**).

Statistical analysis

Unless there is an exceptionally rich source of historical or palæoflood data (see §6.4), statistical analysis of peak flows should play, at most, a minor supporting role in reservoir safety design in the UK. Some relaxation of this recommendation may be possible for minor dams falling in Category D of the ICE guide to floods and reservoir safety (ICE, 1996b). These are: "Special cases where no loss of life can be foreseen as a result of a breach and very little additional flood damage would be caused".

Statistical analysis of gauged flood data sometimes yields a flood frequency distribution that is **bounded above** (see **3** 15). An example is presented in Figure 10.1a. In general, the upper bound to the flood frequency curve should be treated as an artefact of the extreme value analysis. It should never be interpreted as providing an estimate of the PMF.

There are several ways in which an extensive record of flood peaks can be used to refine flood frequency estimates by the rainfall-runoff method (see **4** 7.3.2 and **3** 10), one of which is suitable for use in dam safety assessment. This adjusts key parameters of the rainfall-runoff model by trial and error, until the flood

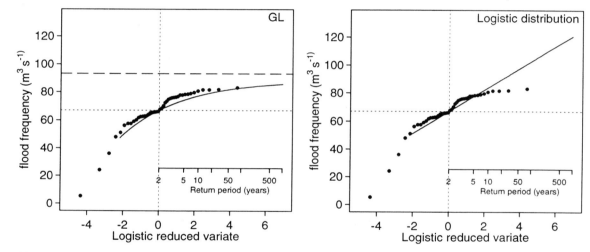

Figure 10.1 *Single-site flood frequency curves for the River Thames at Eynsham (39008) fitted by the method of L-moments: (a) Generalised Logistic distribution, (b) Logistic distribution. The broken line in (a) is the upper bound of the fitted GL distribution. This is illustrative only: refer to Volume 3 for the recommended procedures for statistical flood frequency analysis.*

Box 10.1 Flood frequency curves that imply an upper bound

When a fitted flood frequency curve implies an upper bound, it is not uncommon to find that this is only slightly larger than the largest flood observed in the series. There is no reason to expect that, even within a relatively long period of record of (say) 50 years, conditions should have approached those of the probable maximum event. Examples, such as Figure 10.1, illustrate that extrapolation of a statistical analysis of a gauged record cannot be trusted to provide a sensible estimate of the extreme design floods required in dam safety assessment. Even in less taxing applications (e.g. estimating the 50-year flood), some analysts will feel uncomfortable with the fit provided in Figure 10.1a, and will choose to fit a simpler frequency distribution that avoids the imposition of an upper bound (e.g. Figure 10.1b).

frequency curve synthesised by the rainfall-runoff method is in broad agreement with that derived by statistical analysis. The parameter chosen for adjustment will normally be either the standard percentage runoff (*SPR*) or the unit hydrograph time-to-peak (*Tp*). A catchment for which there is an extensive record of flood peaks may also be amenable to *flood event analysis* (4 2.2 and 4 Appendix A), providing a more direct means of refining estimates of these parameters. Particular judgement is required in cases where there is a large unresolved discrepancy between rainfall-runoff and statistical flood frequency estimates, both of which are based on gauged data. In dam safety applications, the default is usually to adopt the model parameters that yield the higher estimate.

10.2 Other sensitive sites

Special precautions are needed where flooding might lead to a catastrophic loss of control in sensitive operations such as power generation or chemical processing. When supplying a design flood calculation to a client with limited awareness of hydrology, it is important to explain that the meteorological conditions giving rise to an extreme flood will themselves be exceptional, and may disable communication links and stand-by systems.

Other sensitive sites are those that give scope for appreciable ponding of floodwater in extreme conditions, e.g. against an embankment or waste tip, or at a culvert entrance. While it may not always be practical to estimate the risk of flooding leading to structural failure, it is important to assess likely failure modes in the event of an exceptionally extreme flood, and to anticipate their consequences.

10.3 Short-term forecasting of flood risk

It is sometimes necessary to undertake construction/repair works during which an extreme flood presents a special hazard. Knowledge of the seasonal distribution of flood events (see 3 Additional Note 16.1) can be helpful in scheduling works. For most major rivers in the UK, the dominant flood season is October to March, with June and July the least flood-prone months. It is, however, important to note that, on small to medium-sized UK catchments, the *most* extreme floods typically occur in April to September, in consequence of intense convectional storms or mesoscale convective systems (e.g. Gray and Marshall, 1998). Reed and Field (1992) note that, of eight occasions on which heavy rainfall is known to have led to dam safety incidents in the UK between 1875 and 1990, five occurred in the month of July.

It is helpful if work-plans allow the flexibility to advance or defer sensitive stages of the works according to the prevailing river flow conditions. Ettrick *et al.* (1987) and Futter *et al.* (1991) present methods for assessing short-term flood risk to aid such decisions.

10.4 New approaches to reservoir flood estimation

Reed and Field (1992) review several aspects of reservoir flood estimation, and report summary calculations for a subset of UK reservoirs. Reed and Anderson (1992), Anderson and Nadarajah (1993), and Anderson *et al.* (1994) develop an approach to reservoir flood estimation based on joint probability analysis. However, application of the approach demands both a detailed understanding of multivariate statistics, and extensive site-specific datasets of relevant hydrometeorological variables. Joint probability problems are discussed in Appendix B.

Overview

Book VI of Australian Rainfall and Runoff (IE Australia, 1999) recommends using a flood event model (i.e. a rainfall-runoff approach) in reservoir flood design. The book notes that:

The level of uncertainty of these [extreme flood] estimates can only be reduced by long-term fundamental research. Accordingly, it is important that the procedures related to this class of floods be reviewed periodically to ensure that any advances in our understanding of extreme hydrological and hydrometeorological processes are incorporated into design practice.

A wide-ranging review compiled for the US Bureau of Reclamation (USU and USBR, 1999) proposes a new framework for characterising extreme floods for dam safety assessment. The framework seeks to embrace and reconcile different approaches to estimating extreme floods.

Chapter 11 Checklists

New users of the Handbook procedures are encouraged to consult the following boxes as checklists on ideas and understanding.

Box 11.1 Checklist when choosing a method of flood frequency estimation

- Objectives of the study;
- Flood data at subject site;
- Flood data at nearby **donor** sites;
- Flood data for similar, but more distant, **analogue** catchments;
- Other relevant data (e.g. rainfall, soil moisture deficit, ...);
- Background flood history.

Box 11.2 An informal checklist of ideas, issues and resources in flood frequency estimation

Allowance for climate change?	Analogue catchment
Audit trail	Catchment comments
Checking for non-stationary behaviour	Critical duration of rainfall
Digital catchment data	Disparate subcatchments
Donor catchment	Flood defence changes
Flood event data	Flood peak data
Flood rating curves	Historical information
Land-use change	OS maps
Permeable catchments	Previous studies
Reservoir effects	Station comments
Updating flood series	Urban growth since 1990

Box 11.3 Why an audit trail is required

A feature of the FEH flood frequency estimates is that they are dynamic. Estimates by particular methods will change as additional gauged data become available: most obviously, updated flood peak or flood event data for the subject site. However, because of the pooling system used, estimates by the statistical procedure will also change as UK flood peak datasets expand and evolve. This means that it is essential that users provide an audit trail of how they arrived at their final flood frequency estimate.

Chapter 12   Looking ahead

The Handbook sets out procedures to cater for most situations in which flood frequency estimates are required. Much of the material is new, and there is potential for further development, both in the methods themselves and in their application to particular problems.

12.1 Statistical flood frequency estimation

Use of historical data

There is scope to develop better ways of using historical flood data in flood frequency estimation. Combining gauged and historical flood data is somewhat out of fashion, a trend that the Handbook accentuates by typically giving greater emphasis to pooled analyses of flood data than single-site analysis (see §5.3).

Nevertheless, considerable attention is rightly paid to researching flood histories (see Appendix C). Information technology is contributing here, as access and searching facilities become ever more powerful, and libraries and enthusiasts bring local histories and old newspapers into digital form. Archive material from the 18th and 19th centuries is typically both bound and bounded, and it is conceivable that most publications of general interest (for those centuries) will become searchable within the next two decades.

Not counting the number killed, the most reliable historical flood information usually comprises the date and the maximum water level reached. It is suggested that a major initiative is required if historical data are to contribute more fully to flood frequency estimation. Principal requirements are to collate historical information systematically, and to overhaul the theory and practice of relating flood flows and maximum water levels.

Uncertainty

Flood frequency estimation is an inherently uncertain activity. Some guidance to assessing uncertainty in flood frequency estimation is provided in Volume 3. However, the use of pooled frequency analysis methods makes it difficult to assess overall uncertainty in the final estimates. Because of their flexibility, *resampling methods* (see Appendix A) may help in providing approximate confidence intervals for estimates deriving from complicated procedures.

It is recognised that drainage engineers often make an allowance for uncertainty when assessing whether a flood defence will, in performance, meet the intended design standard. The practice is to add a safety margin to the design height of a structure – the so-called *freeboard allowance* – although the amount can be contentious (Kirby and Ash, 1999). Some engineers interpret freeboard as an allowance for defence settlement, errors in construction or wave attack, rather than as a general allowance for uncertainty.

It is to be hoped that those who call for researchers to develop better methods for assessing uncertainty will ensure that, when they arrive, the refinements are well used. One of their most potent uses is in choosing between rival methods of estimation. A more doubtful application is to justify over-design in defiance of benefit-cost efficiency. One hopes that uncertainty measures are not used to justify reductions in data gathering.

Pooling data

It seems likely that the Handbook's advocacy of new methods based on pooling flood peak data from hydrologically similar catchments will stimulate further comment and research.

12.2 Rainfall-runoff methods

A subtext

Users well versed in Flood Studies Report (FSR) methods will recognise that development of the rainfall-runoff method of flood frequency estimation slowed in the 1980s. The technical writing in Volume 4 has striven to make a complicated method easier to understand, and to give clear guidance on best practice in applications. A comprehensive revision of the approach has not been attempted for the Handbook. Such a revision could be quite onerous. A necessary task will be to re-calibrate the 'design package' against best estimates (of flood frequency) for sites with extensive flood peak data. Once procedures are more fully automated, this might be attempted using the new statistical procedures (Volume 3) as a yardstick. However, an important subtext is that the FSR rainfall-runoff method has lost favour with some researchers. Controversy centres on whether the design-event concept (see **4** 3) is convenient and valuable, or constricting and unrealistic.

Some researchers favour an entirely different rainfall-runoff approach to flood frequency estimation, based on the concept of continuous simulation and whole catchment modelling (see §9.6). Others are happy to persist with the design event approach, and to give greater emphasis to hybridisation: combining statistical and rainfall-runoff methods to make the most effective use of available data (see §5.6).

Storm-sewer design and reservoir flood estimation

There are two important applications in which the design event approach remains largely unchallenged: ***storm-sewer design*** and ***reservoir flood estimation***. A principal argument in favour of continuous simulation is the ability to represent soil moisture effects realistically. This avoids the arbitrary assumption about antecedent (i.e. pre-event) wetness that is necessary in a design event method. However, antecedent wetness – or antecedent dryness – is less influential in storm-sewer systems, where the response is typically dominated by runoff from artificial surfaces.

In reservoir flood appraisals, it is pragmatic to assume that the driving force behind the 10000-year flood is the 10000-year extreme rainfall, and to question whether this is reasonably estimated, rather than worry about antecedent wetness effects. It is not so much that the design event approach is well suited to extreme flood estimation as that it is difficult to be convinced that the labour of continuous simulation will be rewarded by a better estimate. Estimating the magnitude of an event with an annual exceedance probability of 10^{-4} is a tough assignment (see Chapter 10). The FSR rainfall-runoff method has the considerable merit of using a unit hydrograph/losses model whose ingredients and workings are reasonably transparent.

A further feature is that flow attenuation effects are important in both storm-sewer and reservoir safety applications. This fits well with the rainfall-runoff method's provision of a design hydrograph, and typically rules out a purely statistical approach to flood frequency estimation.

Both applications are of considerable importance, with flood estimation often underpinning major capital investment in storm-sewer systems and public safety in reservoir flood appraisals. In this context, the current lack of enthusiasm for further research and development of the design event method might be considered a weakness.

12.3 The digital revolution

There is scope to automate flood frequency calculations. This is already possible for basic cases, and it is feasible to develop automated calculations for advanced cases, where best estimates are obtained by combining flood data from many sites. A related opportunity is to develop images that summarise results or help to stimulate fresh thinking about catchment flood behaviour.

The index flood used in the statistical procedures (Volume 3) is the median annual flood, *QMED*. It is the 2-year flood, with an associated annual exceedance probability of 0.5. The blue lines in Figure 12.1 summarise generalised estimates of *QMED* obtained from catchment descriptors (see **3** 13). The position of the blue lines is determined by the digital terrain model, IHDTM, lying behind the FEH catchment descriptors (Volume 5). The blue-line width is proportional to the estimate of $\sqrt{QMED}_{rural}$ obtained from five catchment descriptors. Estimates of *QMED* obtained by direct analysis of gauged flood data are indicated by red dots, with diameter

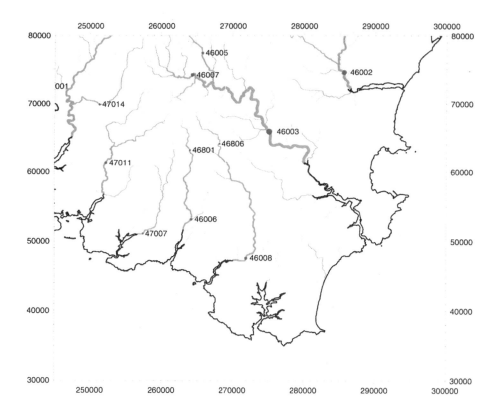

Figure 12.1 *Visualising QMED estimates in a rural part of south Devon. The blue lines are generalised estimates from catchment descriptors; the red symbols denote estimates from flood peak data; line-widths are proportional to $\sqrt{QMED}_{rural}$; symbol widths are proportional to $\sqrt{QMED}$.*

proportional to $\sqrt{QMED}$. The figure suggests that the generalised model underestimates $QMED$ values in this part of south Devon.

Figure 12.2 shows stream networks constructed using the catchment-descriptor model for $QMED_{rural}$. The stream network shown is the union of all nodes for which the $QMED_{rural}$ estimate exceeds a given threshold. In Figure 12.2a,

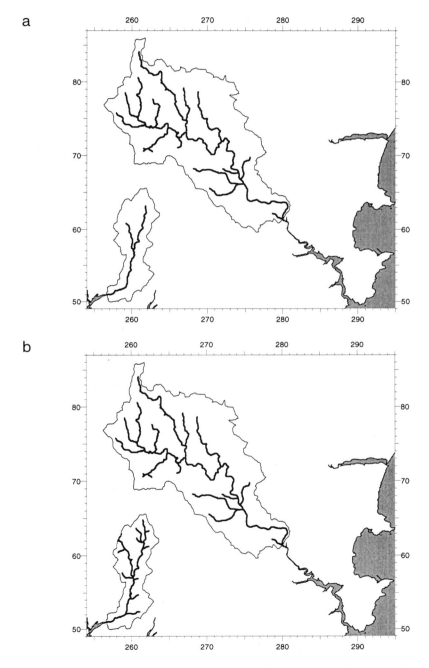

Figure 12.2 *Stream networks constructed from generalised estimates of the index flood. Union of points for which $QMED_{rural}$ is: (a) greater than 10 $m^3 s^{-1}$, (b) greater than 7.7% of the catchment value.*

the threshold is a pre-set discharge. This is analogous to the type of stream network that appears on a conventional map, where the main criterion for marking or omitting a stream is its perennial width. In Figure 12.2b, the threshold is a pre-set fraction of the estimated $QMED_{rural}$ for the given catchment. This device provides a level of detail in the stream network that is tailored to the catchment under investigation. The fraction chosen in Figure 12.2b leaves the stream network unchanged on the larger catchment but provides a more detailed network on the smaller catchment.

There is potential to make rapid progress in these topics, although the most important advance will be to distinguish the useful from the pretty. Judgement will come as experience is gained of the strengths and limitations of automated procedures, and of the digital terrain data on which they rely.

12.4 Catchment description

Floodplain storage is known to influence flood frequency in the middle and lower reaches of larger UK rivers. An outstanding issue is to develop an effective index of floodplain storage, and to consider its use in flood frequency estimation. The index could help to interpret flood growth curves and design hydrographs, and would provide an additional criterion on which to assess catchment similarity when selecting catchments for pooled analysis (see **3** 16).

Section 12.3 suggests a way of summarising stream networks from digital data in a manner independent of the scale at which maps are drawn. This might lead to measures of stream topology and drainage density re-entering the characterisation of catchments.

12.5 Trend detection

Trends in UK flood peaks have been examined by Robson *et al.* (1998), and findings are summarised in Box 12.1. Related studies indicated the greater power of peaks-over-threshold (POT) series, in comparison with annual maximum series, for detecting non-stationary behaviour.

Box 12.1 Trends in UK flood peaks (Robson *et al.*, 1998)

- No significant trends were found in the annual count of peaks-over-threshold (POT) events for 1941-1980 and annual maxima for 1941-1990;

- The confounding effect of climatic variation means that trends associated with land-use change can neither be easily identified nor readily dismissed;

- Even though trend has not been detected, the observed year-to-year fluctuations in the data could have important consequences for flood design and trend analyses;

- Although the study provided no conclusive proof that climatic change has affected fluvial flood behaviour in the UK, this does not mean that effects are not occurring;

- The sensitivity of assessments to climatic conditions in the period of record provides a strong reason for continuing data collection.

Current opinion is that global climate change could lead to significant changes in UK rainfall regimes (see §7.1). Robson *et al.* (1998) have shown the importance of long records, and the value of POT data series, in attempting to detecting underlying trends in the frequency and magnitudes of UK flood peaks. There is scope for a similar study of daily rainfall extremes. This would be facilitated if researchers had unfettered access to UK rainfall records when undertaking strategic studies in the national interest. The power to detect climate change effects on extreme rainfalls would be strengthened by the further computerisation of pre-1961 UK rainfall records.

The ability to anticipate the likely impact of a projected trend in climate or land-use is an important strength of the continuous simulation approach to flood frequency estimation (see §9.6).

12.6 Flood runoff effects of development

Most land-use change has an adverse effect on flood frequency, with urbanisation (4 9.3) the most widespread and dramatic. Current flood frequency estimation methods are not well suited for use in catchment planning and development control (see Chapter 8). While ***whole catchment modelling*** (§9.6) will assist with the former, there is an urgent need for research to underpin design methods for local control of increased runoff arising from development. There is little doubt that greater use should be made of source-control methods, including infiltration drainage (Bettess, 1996). However, research is needed to determine the conditions under which particular remediation techniques succeed or fail.

12.7 Closure

Section 12.1 discusses uncertainty in flood frequency estimates. There is uncertainty also in the political weight attached to flooding and flood risk. Single episodes are capable of changing public perceptions and expectations overnight, as severe flooding in central England and mid Wales demonstrated in April 1998.

To end with an aphorism: extreme events sometimes change ***perceptions*** of flood frequency, and often change ***estimates*** of flood frequency. However, only a change to the catchment itself (e.g. land-use change), or a climatic trend or shift, changes the ***actual*** flood risk. As more data arrive, and better methods evolve, we expect our estimate to approach the actual flood risk more closely.

If there is one factor that acts against this expectation, it is the caprice of climate. At the most basic level: how does one distinguish a river with an inherently volatile flood regime, from one that has simply had a bad run of floods? By introducing pooling-groups based on hydrological similarity rather than geographical region – and providing diagnostic tools – the FEH allows the user to judge whether a catchment may be intrinsically unusual, rather than unusual only in its largest observed floods. Thus, the change of methodology strikes directly at the big issue: "Does the catchment have an unusual flood regime, or has it won the lottery?"

Acknowledgements

The Hadley Centre for Climate Prediction at the Met. Office is thanked for supplying the annual global mean temperature data shown in Figure 7.1. Richard Tabony provided a personal interpretation of global warming effects on UK rainfall regimes, which forms the basis of Box 7.1. The Interlude to this volume was inspired by Forman Acton. Frank Law is thanked for encouraging the greater use of historical data; and Frank, Rory Nathan and David Bowles are thanked for their perspectives on reservoir flood estimation. The digital revolution referred to in Section 12.3 owes much to the long-term work of David Morris in developing digital terrain models for hydrological application.

The account of joint probability problems (Appendix B) has gained from research commissioned by the Department of the Environment (now the Department of the Environment Transport and Regions), the Environment Agency Thames Region (and predecessors), and Halcrow Water. The practical contributions to this topic of Clive Anderson, Stuart Coles, Ian Dwyer, Saraleesan Nadarajah and Jonathan Tawn are gratefully acknowledged. John Packman introduced the authors of Appendix B to the use of dice examples to illustrate joint probability problems.

References

Ackers, P. 1992. *Flood and coastal defence research and development.* Report of the Advisory Committee, MAFF, London.

Acreman, M.C. and Collinge, V.K. 1991. The Calderdale storm revisited. *Proc. BHS 3rd National Hydrology Symp., Southampton,* 4.11-4.16.

Acreman, M.C. and Horrocks, R.J. 1990. Flood frequency analysis for the 1988 Truro floods. *J. Inst. Water & Environ. Manage.* **4**, 62-69.

Acton, F.S. 1970. Interlude: what *not* to compute. In: *Numerical methods that work,* Harper and Row, New York, 245-257.

Anderson, C.W., Dwyer, I.J., Nadarajah, S., Reed, D.W. and Tawn, J.A. 1994. Maximum reservoir water levels. In: *Reservoir safety and the environment* (Ed. British Dam Society), 200-213.

Anderson, C.W. and Nadarajah, S. 1993. Environmental factors affecting reservoir safety. In: Barnett, V. and Turkman, K.F. (Eds), *Statistics for the environment,* John Wiley & Sons, 163-182.

Anon 1993. Urban drainage – the natural way. Hydro Research & Development Ltd., Clevedon.

Archer, D. R. 1992. *Land of singing waters.* Spredden Press, Stocksfield, Northumbria.

Baker, V.R. 1989. Magnitude and frequency of palæofloods. In: Beven, K. and Carling, P.A. (Eds), *Floods: hydrological, sedimentological and geomorphological implications,* John Wiley & Sons, 171-183.

Barnett, V. and Lewis, T. 1984. *Outliers in statistical data.* 2nd edition. John Wiley.

Bettess, R. 1996. *Infiltration drainage – manual of good practice.* CIRIA Report R156, Construction Industry Research and Information Association, London.

Black, A.R. 1996. Major flooding and increased flood frequency in Scotland since 1988. *Phys. Chem. Earth* **20**, 463-468.

Boorman, D.B., Hollis, J.M. and Lilly, A. 1995. *Hydrology of soil types: a hydrologically-based classification of the soils of the United Kingdom.* Report 126, Institute of Hydrology, Wallingford, UK.

British Rainfall (various dates from 1919). Published by HMSO.

Bulman, R.B. 1984. *Prodigal rainfall and flood estimation.* R. Bulman, 29 Fisher Street, Carlisle, UK.

Burroughs, W.J. 1992. *Weather cycles: real or imaginary?* Cambridge University Press.

Calver, A. and Lamb, R. 1996. Flood frequency estimation using continuous rainfall-runoff modelling. *Phys. Chem. Earth* **20**, 479-483.

Carling, P.A. and Grodek, T. 1994. Indirect estimation of ungauged peak discharges in a bedrock channel with reference to design discharge selection. *Hydrol. Proc.* **8**, 497-511.

Coles, S.G. and Tawn, J.A. 1994. Statistical methods for multivariate extremes: an application to structural design (with discussion). *Applied Statistics,* **43**, 1-48.

Crooks, S.M. 1994. Changing flood peak levels on the River Thames. *Proc. Instn. Civ. Engrs, Wat. Marit. & Energy* **106**, 267-279.

Currie, R.G. 1987. Examples and implications of 18.6- and 11-year terms in world weather records. In: Rampino, M.R., Sanders, J.E., Newman, W.S. and Konigsson, L.K. (Eds) *Climate: History, periodicity and predictability,* Van Nostrand Reinhold, 378-403.

Dales, M.Y. and Reed, D.W. 1989. *Regional flood and storm hazard assessment.* IH Report No. 102, Institute of Hydrology, Wallingford.

Dixon, M.J. and Tawn, J.A. 1994. *Extreme sea-levels at the UK A-class sites: site-by-site analysis.* Internal Document No. 65, Proudman Oceanographic Laboratory, Birkenhead.

Efron, B. 1982. *The jackknife, the bootstrap and other resampling plans.* SIAM Regional Conf. Series in Applied Maths, 38. Philadelphia.

Ettrick, T.M., Mawdsley, J.A. and Metcalfe, A.V. 1987. The influence of catchment antecedent conditions on seasonal flood risk. *Water Resour. Res.* **23**, 481-488.

Faulkner, D.S. and Jones, D.A. 1999. The FORGEX method of rainfall growth estimation, III: Examples and confidence intervals. *Hydrol. and Earth Systems Sciences* **3**, 205-212.

Ferguson, T.S. 1961. On the rejection of outliers. *Proc. 4th Berkeley Symp. on Mathematical Statistics and Probability*, **1**, 253-287.

Fisher, N.I. 1993. *Statistical analysis of circular data*. Cambridge Univ. Press.

Fuller, R.M., Groom, G.B. and Jones, A.R. 1994. The Land Cover Map of Great Britain: an automated classification of Landsat Thematic Mapper data. *Photogrammetric Eng. & Remote Sensing*, **60**, 533-562.

Futter, M.R., Mawdsley, J.A. and Metcalfe, A.V. 1991. Short term flood risk prediction: a comparison of the Cox regression model and a conditional distribution model. *Water Resour. Res.* **27**, 1649-1656.

Goodess, C.M. and Palutikof, J.P. 1998. Development of daily rainfall scenarios for southeast Spain using a circulation-type approach to downscaling. *Int. J. Climatol.* **10**, 1051-1083.

Gray, M.E.B. and Marshall, C. 1998. Mesoscale convective systems over the UK, 1981-97. *Weather* **53**, 388-396.

Gregory, K.J., Lewin, J. and Thornes, J.B. (Eds) 1987. *Palaeohydrology in practice*. John Wiley & Sons.

Grew, H. and Werritty, A. 1995. Changes in flood frequency and magnitude in Scotland 1964-1992. *Proc. BHS 5th National Hydrology Symp., Edinburgh*, 3.1-3.9.

Hall, M.J. 1984. *Urban hydrology*. Elsevier.

Hawkes, P. and Hague, R. 1994. *Validation of joint probability methods for large waves and high water levels*. Report SR 347, HR Wallingford Ltd.

Hollis, G.E. 1974. The effect of urbanization on floods in the Canon's Brook, Harlow, Essex. In: *Fluvial processes in instrumented watersheds* (Eds K. Gregory and D.E. Walling), Inst. Brit. Geogr., Special Publ. No. 6, 123-140.

Hosking, J.R.M. and Wallis, J.R. 1997. *Regional frequency analysis: an approach based on L-moments*. Cambridge University Press.

Houghton, J.T., Meira Filho, L.G., Callander, B.A., Harris, N., Kattenberg, A. and Maskell, K. 1996. Summary for policymakers. In: *Climate change 1995: the science of climate change* (Eds *as authors*), Cambridge University Press, 1-7.

Hulme, M. and Jenkins, G.J. 1998. Climate change scenarios for the UK: scientific report. UKCIP Tech. Report No. 1, Climatic Research Unit, Norwich.

Ibidapo-Obe, O. and Beran, M. 1988. *Hydrological aspects of combined effects of storm surges and heavy rainfall on river flow*. WMO Operational Hydrol. Report No. 30, Publ. No. 704, World Meteorological Organization, Geneva.

ICE 1978. *Floods and reservoir safety: an engineering guide*. Institution of Civil Engineers, London.

ICE 1996a. *Land drainage and flood defence responsibilities: a practical guide*. 3rd edition. Institution of Civil Engineers, London.

ICE 1996b. *Floods and reservoir safety: an engineering guide*. 3rd edition. Institution of Civil Engineers, London.

IE Australia 1999. Estimation of large and extreme floods. Book VI, Volume 1, *Australian Rainfall and Runoff – a guide to flood estimation* (Revised edition), Institution of Engineers, Australia.

IH (various dates). *Flood Studies Supplementary Reports*. Institute of Hydrology, Wallingford.

IH 1979. *Design flood estimation in catchments subject to urbanisation*. Flood Studies Supplementary Report No. 5, Institute of Hydrology, Wallingford.

Jack, W.L. 1981. Rainfall return periods for December 1979. *Weather* **36**, 274-276.

Jervoise, E. 1930. *The ancient bridges of the South of England*. Architectural Press, London.

Jervoise, E. 1931a. *The ancient bridges of Mid and Eastern England*. Architectural Press, London.

Jervoise, E. 1931b. *The ancient bridges of the North of England*. Architectural Press, London.

Jones, D.A. 1998. *Joint probability fluvial-tidal analyses: structure functions and historical emulation.* Report to MAFF, Institute of Hydrology, Wallingford.

Jones, P.D., Ogilvie, A.E. and Wigley, T.M.L. 1984. *River-flow data for the UK: reconstructed data back to 1844 and historical data back to 1556.* Climatic Research Unit report, Norwich.

Kirby, A.M. and Ash, J.R.V. 1999. *Fluvial freeboard guidance note.* R&D Technical Report W187, Environment Agency, Bristol.

Knight, C. 1979. Urbanization and natural stream channel morphology: the case of two English towns. In: Hollis, G.E. (Ed.), *Man's impact on the hydrological cycle in the United Kingdom*, Geo Abstracts Ltd, Norwich, 181-198.

Lamb, H.H. 1972. *Climate: present, past and future.* Volume 1: Fundamentals and climate now. Methuen, London.

Leese, M.N. 1973. The use of censored data in the estimation of Gumbel distribution parameters for annual maximum flood series. *Wat. Resour. Res.* **9**, 1534-1542.

Lowing, M.J. 1995. *Linkage of flood frequency curve with maximum flood estimate.* Foundation for Water Research, Marlow.

MAFF 1993. *Flood and coastal defence: project appraisal guidance notes.* Publication 1214, Ministry of Agriculture, Fisheries & Food, London.

Marshall, D.C.W. and Bayliss, A.C. 1994. *Flood estimation for small catchments.* IH Report No. 124, Institute of Hydrology, Wallingford.

May, B.R. 1985. The London Weather Radar Project. *Circulation* No. 6, 6-7. British Hydrological Society.

Metcalfe, A.V. 1997. *Statistics in civil engineering.* Arnold.

Morris, D.G. and Flavin, R.W. 1996. *Flood risk map for England and Wales.* IH Report No. 130, Institute of Hydrology, Wallingford.

Murphy, I. 1993. The impact of the environment: the shock of the new. In: Farmer, B. and Louw, H. (Eds). *Companion to contemporary architectural thought*

Naden, P.S., Calver, A., Samuels, P. and Ash, J. 1997. *Whole catchment modelling: the basis for an integrated approach to catchment management.* Report to MAFF, Institute of Hydrology, Wallingford.

Naden, P.S. and McCartney, M.P. 1991. *Direct estimation of flood depth.* Report to MAFF, Institute of Hydrology, Wallingford.

National Water Council 1981. *Design and analysis of urban storm drainage – the Wallingford procedure.* National Water Council, London.

NERC 1975. *Flood Studies Report* (in five volumes). Natural Environment Research Council, London.

Ostenaa, D.A., Levish, D.R., O'Connell, D.R.H. and Cohn, E.A. 1997. *Paleoflood study for Causey and Pineview Dams.* Seismotectonic Rep. No. 96-6, Bureau of Reclamation, US Dept of the Interior, Denver, Colorado.

Packman, J.C. 1980. *The effects of urbanization on flood magnitude and flood frequency.* IH Report No. 63, Institute of Hydrology, Wallingford.

Pegram, G. and Adamson, P. 1988. Revised risk analysis for extreme storms and floods in Natal/KwaZulu. *Die Siviele Ingenieur in Suid-Afrika*, Jan. 1988, 15-20 and 42. (Discussion: Jul. 1988, 331-226)

Pirt, J. 1975. *The Hebden flood, 13th August 1975.* Internal report, Resource Planning, Yorkshire Water Authority.

Potter, H. 1978. *The use of historic records for the augmentation of hydrological data.* IH Report No. 46, Institute of Hydrology, Wallingford.

Pugh, D.T. and Vassie, J.M. 1980. Applications of the joint probability method of extreme sea level computations. *Proc. Instn Civil Engineers*, Part 2, **69**, 959-975.

Reed, D.W. 1987. Engaged on the ungauged: Applications of the FSR rainfall-runoff method. *Proc. BHS National Hydrology Symp., Hull*, 2.1-2.19.

Reed, D.W. 1992. Triggers to severe floods: extreme rainfall and antecedent wetness. In: Parr, N.M., Charles, J.A. and Walker, S. (Eds), *Water resources and reservoir engineering*, Thomas Telford Ltd, London, 219-228.

Reed, D.W. 1994. Plans for the Flood Estimation Handbook. *Proc. MAFF Conf. of River and Coastal Engineers, Loughborough*, MAFF, London, 8.3.1-8.3.8.

Reed, D.W. and Anderson, C.W. 1992. A statistical perspective on reservoir flood standards. In: Parr, N.M., Charles, J.A. and Walker, S. (Eds), *Water resources and reservoir engineering*, Thomas Telford Ltd, London, 229-239.

Reed, D.W. and Dwyer, I.J. 1996. Flood estimation at confluences: ideals and trials. *Proc. MAFF Conf. of River and Coastal Engineers, Keele*, MAFF, London, 3.2.1-3.2.10.

Reed, D.W. and Field, E.K. 1992. *Reservoir flood estimation: another look*. IH Report No. 114, Institute of Hydrology, Wallingford.

Reed, D.W. and Stewart, E.J. 1991. Discussion on dam safety: an evaluation of some procedures for design flood estimation. *Hydrol. Sci. J.* **36**, 499-502.

Reynard, N.S., Prudhomme, C. and Crooks, S.M. 1998. Impacts of climate change on the flood characteristics of the Thames and Severn rivers. In: *Impact of climate change on flooding and sustainable river management*, Proc. 2nd RIBAMOD Workshop, February 1998, Wallingford.

Robinson, D.N. 1995. *The Louth flood of 29th May 1920*. Louth Naturalists' Antiquarian and Literary Society, Louth, 36pp.

Robson, A.J., Jones, T.K., Reed, D.W. and Bayliss, A.C. 1998. A study of trend and variation in UK floods. *Int. J. Climatol.* **18**, 165-182.

Rodda, J.C. 1976. Basin studies. Chapter 10 in: Rodda, J.C. (Ed.), *Facets in hydrology*, John Wiley & Sons, 257-297.

Scott, D.W. 1992. *Multivariate density estimation: theory, practice and visualization*. John Wiley & Sons.

SEPA/EA 1997. *A guide to sustainable urban drainage*. Scottish Environment Protection Agency, Stirling; Environment Agency, Bristol.

Symons, G.J. 1892. *Symons's monthly meteorological magazine*, 148-153.

Thompson, G. and Law, F.M. 1983. An assessment of the fluvial tidal flooding problem of the River Ancholme, UK. IUGG Interdisciplinary Symp. on *Assessment of natural hazards*, Hamburg, 12pp.

USU and USBR 1999. *A framework for characterizing extreme floods for dam safety risk assessment*. Utah State University and the US Bureau of Reclamation, Denver, Colorado.

Walling, D.E. 1979. The hydrological impact of building activity: a study near Exeter. In: Hollis, G.E. (Ed.), *Man's impact on the hydrological cycle in the United Kingdom*, Geo Abstracts Ltd, Norwich, 135-151.

Wharton, G. 1989. *River discharge estimated from river channel dimensions in Britain*. PhD thesis, Dept of Geography, University of Southampton.

Whitehead, P.G, and Robinson, M. 1993. Experimental basin studies – an international and historical perspective of forest impacts. *J. Hydrol.* **145**, 217-230.

Wilby, R.L., Wigley, T.M.L., Conway, D., Jones, P.D., Hewitson, B.C., Main, J. and Wilks, D.S. 1998. Statistical downscaling of general circulation model output: a comparison of methods. *Water Resour. Res.* **34**, 2995-3008.

Yevjevich, V. 1991. Tendencies in hydrology research and its applications for the 21st century. *Water Resour. Manage.* **5**, 1-23.

Appendix A Return period, risk and resampling

This appendix introduces some statistical terminology and concepts used in the Handbook. Sections A.1 and A.2 discuss the meaning of return periods and how to assess the risk of experiencing a rare flood within a given timeframe. Section A.3 introduces the less familiar topic of resampling methods.

A.1 Return period

The return period is a measure of the rarity of an event: the longer the return period, the rarer the event. The return period is sometimes referred to as the recurrence interval. Formally, there are two definitions of the return period of a flood peak Q:

- The return period on the peaks-over-threshold (POT) scale, T_{POT}, is the average interval between floods exceeding Q;

- The return period on the annual maximum scale, T_{AM}, is the average interval between years containing one or more floods greater than Q.

T_{POT} is the more precise definition of flood rarity, since it considers all large floods. However, for many purposes, it is convenient to use T_{AM}.

The difference between T_{AM} and T_{POT} is generally unimportant for return periods longer than about 20 years. When required at shorter return periods, values can be exchanged using Langbein's formula, which can be written:

$$1/T_{AM} \approx 1 - \exp(-1/T_{POT}) \qquad \text{or} \qquad 1/T_{POT} \approx -\ln(1 - 1/T_{AM})$$

It is important to remember that T_{AM} represents the average interval between years containing large floods, not the average interval between large floods. There is always an interval of one year between one year and the next. Thus, T_{AM} never takes a value less than 1.0. The reciprocal, $1/T_{AM}$, can be interpreted as the annual exceedance probability. For UK conditions, there is generally no serial dependence in annual maxima, i.e. floods in one year are unrelated to floods in the previous year. Thus, the ***annual exceedance probability*** (AEP) defines the probability that a flood greater than Q will occur during any one year.

In the FEH, return period is generally measured on the annual maximum scale, and the notation T_{AM} is abbreviated to T. The flood peak with a return period of T years is denoted by Q_T, and referred to as the ***T-year flood***.

A.2 Risk equation

In assessing flood risk, it is helpful to be able to relate the design standard – expressed as a return period T – to the risk of a ***design exceedance*** within a lifetime of interest. Usually, this will be the intended working life of the structure, but evaluations using the intended working life of its designer may also be of interest! It can be shown (see **3** Additional Note 11.1) that the risk, r, of experiencing one or more exceedances of the T-year flood in a period of M years is:

$$r = 1 - (1 - 1/T)^M \qquad\qquad\qquad (A.1)$$

The risk equation reveals some curious properties. A risk of 0.5 represents an even chance. Thus, the rarity of the flood that has an even chance of being experienced at least once in M years is found by solving:

$$0.5 = 1 - (1 - 1/T)^M$$

This yields:

$$T = 1/(1 - 0.5^{1/M})$$

For example, the flood with an even chance of being experienced at least once in 50 years is the 73-year flood. In general, the expected largest flood in a period of M years has a return period about 1.45 to 1.50 times M years, for the record lengths typically of interest (1.5 applies when $M = 10$, 1.45 applies when $M > 50$).

The probability of experiencing the 100-year flood **at least once** in 100 years can be found by setting $T = 100$ and $M = 100$ in Equation A.1, yielding:

$$r = 1 - (1 - 1/100)^{100} = 0.63$$

For most values of T of interest, there is a risk of nearly two-thirds of experiencing a flood worse than the T-year flood in a period of T years.

A.3 Resampling methods

The conventional approach to assessing uncertainty is to make a distributional assumption (e.g. that the logarithms of annual maximum floods are Normally distributed) and to estimate the uncertainty in the statistic of interest (e.g. the mean) using a theoretical formula. This approach can have disadvantages: the assumption may be unreasonable, it may not be uniquely appropriate (i.e. another assumption might be equally reasonable), and the user needs to know the relevant theoretical formula. In some situations, there may not be a workable theoretical solution.

Resampling methods offer an alternative approach to assessing uncertainty. The methods include *permutation testing*, *boot-strapping* and *jack-knifing*, and have potentially wide application in hydrology. They can also be used to explore the significance of differences between datasets, and to test for possible trend. They have three particular merits: the basic concept is relatively simple, they require relatively little specialist skill to apply, and they are non-parametric. The last feature means that no assumption is required about the parent distribution from which the data sample is thought to derive. Although not a cure-all, resampling methods allow the non-specialist to get some idea about uncertainties. The resampling approach does not feature in older statistical textbooks because the methods were impractical before the advent of very powerful computers.

A.3.1 Where resampling methods can help

Exploring uncertainty Consider the case where a measure, such as the median annual flood (*QMED*) or the average unit hydrograph time-to-peak (*Tp*), has been estimated from a relatively small or highly variable sample of data. Resampling can explore the *sampling error*, i.e. the uncertainty in the estimate that arises from evaluating the measure from a relatively small or highly variable data sample (see §A.3.4).

Assessing differences Another question that can arise is whether two catchments, or two sets of flood data, exhibit a significant difference. Resampling cannot judge whether the aspect of hydrological behaviour selected is the most relevant, or whether the chosen measure has characterised it adequately. But resampling can allow a test to be made of whether, in terms of the chosen measure, the two data samples are significantly different (see §A.3.5).

Checking for trend A further question is whether time-series data exhibit trend. Resampling cannot judge whether a trend reflects natural variability or systematic change. However, permutation methods can test whether an ***apparent*** trend could have arisen by chance (see §A.3.3).

A.3.2 Balanced resampling in brief

Resampling methods assume that the sample of data provides all that is known about the variable. Each observation is assumed to be of equal importance. The basic idea of resampling is to use the observed sample to generate additional hypothetical samples, or ***resamples***. The uncertainty in the statistic of interest for the observed sample is then judged by looking at the variability of the statistic across all the resamples.

Resamples are formed by random selection from the observed sample. There are several ways of arranging this. In ***balanced resampling***, the N values comprising the observed sample are replicated B times. A typical choice for B is 199 or 1999. The replicated datasets are then merged to provide a super-sample of BN values. These values are randomly re-ordered (i.e. mixed up) and re-divided into B samples of size N. Balanced resampling gets its name because, when the resamples are considered as a batch, each of the observed data values appears the same number of times. This evenhandedness is not achieved in simpler resampling schemes such as ***sampling with replacement***, in which the resamples are obtained by repeated sampling from the actual dataset of size N, the selected observation being immediately returned to the pool so that it is available for reselection.

The analysis proceeds by deriving the statistic of interest for each resample in turn. A confidence interval for the statistic is obtained by ordering the derived statistics by magnitude, and counting in from either end. For example, the 95% confidence interval is delimited by the 5th smallest and 5th largest of 199 values, or by the 50th smallest and 50th largest values of 1999 resamples (but see also §A.3.6).

A strength of the resampling approach is that it can be applied to construct a confidence interval for an unusual or unfamiliar statistic, in circumstances where a theoretical solution may be difficult or impractical.

A.3.3 Checking for trend by permutation testing

Consider a flood series that provides annual maxima for m years $\{Q_1, Q_2, \ldots Q_t, \ldots Q_m\}$, where the subscript t reminds that the values are in time sequence rather than ordered by magnitude. An example is provided in Figure A.1. Does the time-series exhibit long-term trend?

One approach is to fit a least-squares regression line, and to test whether the gradient is significantly different from zero. The test requires several assumptions, one of which is that the residuals from the regression line are Normally distributed. ***Permutation testing*** avoids making this last assumption. The ***null hypothesis*** is the default behaviour to be tested. In this case, the null hypothesis is that there

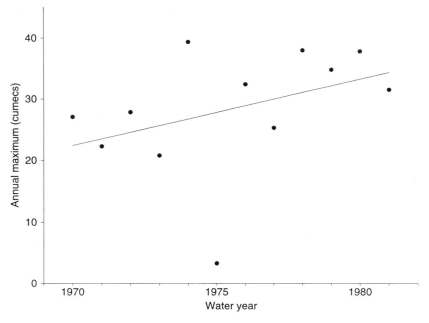

Figure A.1 *Time-series of annual maximum floods, Welland at Ashley (31021); the fitted line is derived by ordinary least-squares regression*

is no trend. If this is true, any permutation of the data is as equally likely to have occurred as the actual observed sequence.

In the permutation approach, the observed sequence of data values is permuted at random, and the regression analysis repeated. By making many such experiments (perhaps analysing 199 or 1999 permuted samples), it is possible to judge whether the regression gradient for the observed sequence is unusually high or low. If a 95% significance level is used, the gradient would be judged significantly different from zero if it lies in the top 2.5% or the bottom 2.5% of those found in the permutation experiments. Where 1999 permutations have been used, the relevant comparisons are with the 50th highest and the 50th lowest of the 1999 experimental gradients.

The avoidance of having to assume that the residuals about the regression line are Normally distributed seems to be a relatively small prize. In the case of the 12-year annual maximum series for the Welland at Ashley (Figure A.1), the trend is judged to be statistically insignificant (at the 95% level), by either approach. The example illustrates the extent to which the eye sees a trend but does not readily register that it may have arisen by chance.

The permutation approach comes into its own when testing a group of data series for joint evidence of long-term trend. For example, Robson *et al.* (1998) test for trends in the number of peaks-over-threshold (POT) flood events in the UK as a whole. This is achieved by permuting the data in year-blocks: a device that preserves the inter-site dependence evident in the real data.

The permutation approach can also be used to test the significance of a sudden change, or ***step-change***, in a time-series. In this case, the statistic of interest might be taken to be the difference between the means of the first and second halves of the time-series. This is a slightly less-well behaved problem. If the apparent step-change has arisen by chance, its position in the sequence is of no significance. Thus, choosing to break the time-series into two at the position of the apparent break-point introduces a small bias which means that the null hypothesis will be rejected slightly too easily.

A.3.4 Exploring uncertainty in a flood statistic

The flood record for the Bourne at Hadlow (40006) is 29 years long. This sounds to be long enough to provide a relatively good estimate of the mean annual flood *QBAR*, but how good?

For this station, annual maximum flood peak data are available for 29 years (see Appendix B of Volume 3). The mean annual flood is estimated as the arithmetic mean of the 29 values, yielding *QBAR* = 9.41 m³s⁻¹. Figure A.2 illustrates the values of *QBAR* obtained from 199 balanced resamples (see §A.3.2). The 5th smallest and 5th largest values provide an approximate 95% confidence interval for the estimate of (6.92, 13.56) m³s⁻¹ or (9.41 – 2.49, 9.41 + 4.15) m³s⁻¹. For somewhat obscure reasons (see §A.3.6), it is appropriate to reverse the confidence intervals to yield (9.41 – 4.15, 9.41 + 2.49) m³s⁻¹ or (5.26, 11.90) m³s⁻¹.

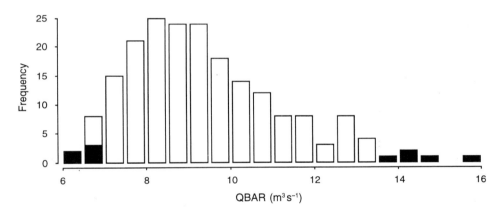

Figure A.2   *Empirical distribution of resampled QBAR values for the Bourne at Hadlow (40006); the estimates derive from a 29-year annual maximum series; the five highest and five lowest of the 199 resampled values are shaded.*

Confidence intervals obtained by resampling are not unique. Table A.1 illustrates the confidence intervals obtained in three different trials using 199 resamples, and a fourth trial using 1999 resamples.

The right-hand column of Table A.1 presents 95% confidence intervals for the median annual flood, *QMED*. This is the index flood adopted in the FEH. For records longer than 13 years, *QMED* is generally estimated as the sample median of the annual maxima. In this example, there are an odd number of annual maxima, and the median always coincides with one of the flood values in the observed series. In consequence, so too do the upper and lower confidence limits. This explains the limited variety of confidence intervals found in the four trials.

The Bourne at Hadlow flood series illustrates one of the reasons why the FEH prefers to use *QMED* rather than *QBAR* as the index flood. The series includes

Table A.1 *Confidence intervals for QMED and QBAR, Bourne at Hadlow (40006), derived by balanced resampling and reversal technique (see §A.3.6); in the 'varied 4th' trial, an exceptional annual maximum is omitted.*

Trial	Number of resamples	Estimate and 95% confidence interval for QBAR $(m^3 s^{-1})$	Estimate and 95% confidence interval for QMED $(m^3 s^{-1})$
1st	199	9.41 (5.26, 11.90)	6.77 (3.81, 8.02)
2nd	199	9.41 (5.39, 12.18)	6.77 (3.81, 8.02)
3rd	199	9.41 (5.34, 12.01)	6.77 (3.81, 8.16)
4th	1999	9.41 (5.44, 12.10)	6.77 (3.81, 8.02)
Varied 4th	1999	7.73 (6.38, 9.03)	6.64 (5.52, 9.73)

the exceptional flood of 15 September 1968 (estimated peak of 56.6 $m^3 s^{-1}$). The bottom row in the table shows the estimates (and confidence intervals) when *QMED* and *QBAR* are evaluated from 28 annual maxima, omitting the exceptional value of 56.6 $m^3 s^{-1}$. Whereas the sample mean (*QBAR*) changes from 9.41 to 7.73 $m^3 s^{-1}$, the sample median (*QMED*) changes only from 6.77 to 6.64 $m^3 s^{-1}$. This reflects the fact that the median is an intrinsically more stable (or robust) measure than the mean; i.e. it is less sensitive to unusual data values.

A.3.5 Assessing differences in flood seasonality

The flood record for the Skerne at Preston le Skerne (25020) is 16 years long. There is a much longer record for the nearby Browney at Burn Hall (24005). Are the catchments sufficiently similar to justify using station 25020 as a donor catchment (see §3.3) when estimating flood frequency at Preston le Skerne? One way of assessing the similarity of flood behaviour is to compare the seasonality of flooding at the two sites.

Figure A.3 illustrates the dates of the 48 largest floods recorded in the 16 water-years commencing 1 October 1976. This is the period of record in common between the two stations. The cross-hair in each diagram denotes the centroid of

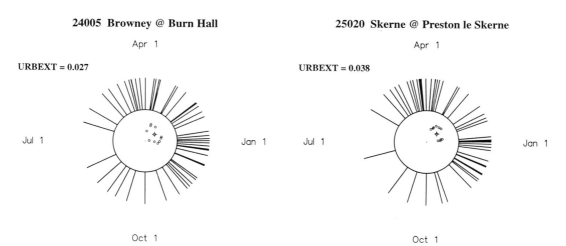

Figure A.3 *Informal 95% confidence zones for flood seasonality, constructed by balanced resampling*

the flood dates for the observed sample (see **3** Additional Note 16.1). The other symbols denote the ten most distant centroids for 199 balanced resamples (see §A.3.2), and indicate an informal 95% confidence zone for the centroid of flood dates. Neither centroid falls outside the confidence zone constructed for the other station. Thus there is no evidence to suggest that the flood seasonalities are significantly different, encouraging use of station 24005 as a donor catchment for estimating floods at Preston le Skerne.

A more formal approach would derive a confidence interval for the difference in centroids expressed as a vector, using balanced resampling across years.

A.3.6 Interval reversal when constructing confidence intervals by balanced resampling

The argument for interval reversal is as follows, based on Faulkner and Jones (1999). Analysis of the original sample yields the value X_{sam} for the statistic being considered. The resampling experiments suggest that, if X_{sam} were the true value, 95% of sample values would lie in (X_L, X_U), where X_L and X_U are the lower and upper percentile values derived from resampling. Hence, 95% of **errors** are expected to lie in the range $(X_L - X_{sam}, X_U - X_{sam})$. However, for the original dataset, the real error is $X_{sam} - X_{true}$. Hence, in 95% of cases, $X_{sam} - X_{true}$ lies in $(X_L - X_{sam}, X_U - X_{sam})$. It follows that in 95% of cases, $X_{true} - X_{sam}$ lies in $(X_{sam} - X_U, X_{sam} - X_L)$, confirming that the intervals are reversed to that intuitively expected. When following this approach, it is convenient to construct the confidence interval as $(2X_{sam} - X_U, 2X_{sam} - X_L)$.

A.3.7 Further information

Efron (1982) introduces resampling methods. The concept of balanced resampling, and applications to circular data (e.g. Figure A.3), are discussed by Fisher (1993). Balanced resampling is used in Volume 2 to derive confidence intervals for rainfall growth estimates, based on Faulkner and Jones (1999).

Permutation sampling is used in Volume 3 Chapter 21 to check for non-stationary effects (i.e. trend and step-changes) in individual flood series. Recommendations are also made for testing for regional trend in flood behaviour, based on Robson *et al.* (1998).

Appendix B   Joint probability problems

Joint probability is a convenient label for a difficult type of problem in engineering design in which a critical condition depends on two or more input factors. Hydrological examples include extreme water level estimation in a tidally influenced river and flood frequency estimation downstream of a confluence. Where possible, it may be sensible to avoid joint probability problems (see Section B.5) or to engage an expert. This appendix seeks to illustrate why joint probability problems are difficult to solve, and to introduce something of their language and properties to a wider audience. Pugh and Vassie (1980), Ibidapo-Obe and Beran (1988), Coles and Tawn (1994), Dixon and Tawn (1994) and Jones (1998) provide important treatments, but none is both definitive and digestible.

B.1 Some examples

In the more obvious joint probability problems, the critical condition has more than one prime cause. For example, an extreme water level at a confluence of tributaries arises when one or both rivers are in spate. Another example is in a river's tidal reach, in which flooding arises from a river flood, a surge tide, or a combination of high river-flow and high tide. A less familiar example is river flooding on a catchment prone to snowmelt, where floods arise from rainfall, snowmelt or a combination of rainfall and snowmelt.

In other joint probability problems, the critical condition has only one prime cause but the impact is strongly influenced by secondary factors. For example, maximum water levels in a tide-locked storm-sewer system are produced by heavy rain in the drainage area. The state of the tide has an important influence on the maximum water level reached but cannot alone cause a flood. Another example is wind-induced wave run-up on the shore of a lake. While an extreme wind speed is required for a critical condition, the wind direction strongly influences the impact. A slightly less familiar example is river flooding on a highly permeable catchment, for which the flood impact of heavy rain is strongly influenced by concurrent groundwater, and/or soil-water, conditions.

Table B.1 *A classification of joint probability problems*

Type A: More than one prime cause	Type B: One prime cause but one or more secondary factors
Water level at a river confluence	Wind-induced wave run-up on a lake
Water level in a tidally influenced river	Water level in a tide-locked sewer system
River flooding on a catchment prone to snowmelt	River flooding on a highly permeable catchment

Where there is a long record of the variable representing the ***effect*** – typically a river flow or water level – its bivariate origin (i.e. the two ***causal*** variables) may appear to be of little consequence. However, even in such a fortunate case, a joint probability study may be important to understand the range of scenarios under which extreme values have occurred or might occur.

B.2 Dice problems

The risk of experiencing a flood can be likened to the throw of a die. In any one year, there is a $1/T$ probability of experiencing one or more floods bigger than the T-year event (see Section A.1). The fundamental difficulty with joint probability problems is that nature is throwing more than one die.

It is sometimes said that the key to solving joint probability problems is to determine whether the input factors act independently. Certainly, it is helpful if they are known to act independently, or can be shown to act effectively independently. However, even where the input factors are truly independent, solutions are rarely straightforward.

The throw of two dice

Dice experiments provide readily understood examples which highlight some of the principles of solving joint probability problems, as well as their pitfalls. Example B.1 introduces the concept of the **structure function**. This is the function that defines the relationship that the output variable (e.g. water level at site of interest) takes to the input variables (e.g. tide level and river flow). The example demonstrates how the risk can be evaluated by considering all the possible combinations of input values. The method is often called the **matrix method**. This is a somewhat misleading name, since two matrices are always involved. Hence, it is here termed the **double matrix method**. The two matrices for Example B.1 are given as Tables B.2 and B.3.

Example B.1 What is the risk of scoring 11 or more with a dice pair?

Let x_1 denote the throw of the first die, x_2 the throw of the second die, and y their combined score. The relationship between the input variables, x_1 and x_2, and the output variable, y, is known as the **structure function**. In this case it is:

$$y = x_1 + x_2$$

The problem is solved by **considering all the possibilities**. In this case there are 36 (6^2) possible outcomes of the throw of the dice pair (see Table B.2), each of which is equally likely (see Table B.3). The three outcomes of interest are highlighted in the tables. Using Pr(...) to denote probability:

$$\begin{aligned}
\Pr(y \geq 11) &= \Pr(y = 11) + \Pr(y = 12) \\
&= \Pr(x_1 = 6 \ \& \ x_2 = 5) + \Pr(x_1 = 5 \ \& \ x_2 = 6) + \Pr(x_1 = 6 \ \& \ x_2 = 6) \\
&= (1/6).(1/6) + (1/6).(1/6) + (1/6).(1/6) \\
&= 1/12
\end{aligned}$$

Thus, a combined score of 11 or more is a 1-in-12 event. Strictly, to distinguish an unusually high score from an unusually low score, this should be referred to as the 1-in-12 maximum event. To recap, only three of the 36 possible outcomes of shaking two dice yield a score of 11 or greater. So the risk of scoring 11 or more is 3/36 or 1/12.

Table B.2 *Matrix of output values, y, where y = x_1 + x_2, and x_1 and x_2 are dice inputs; this defines the structure function for Example B.1*

	x_1 = 1	x_1 = 2	x_1 = 3	x_1 = 4	x_1 = 5	x_1 = 6
x_2 = 1	y = 2	y = 3	y = 4	y = 5	y = 6	y = 7
x_2 = 2	y = 3	y = 4	y = 5	y = 6	y = 7	y = 8
x_2 = 3	y = 4	y = 5	y = 6	y = 7	y = 8	y = 9
x_2 = 4	y = 5	y = 6	y = 7	y = 8	y = 9	y = 10
x_2 = 5	y = 6	y = 7	y = 8	y = 9	y = 10	y = 11
x_2 = 6	y = 7	y = 8	y = 9	y = 10	y = 11	y = 12

Table B.3 *Matrix of probabilities; independent and unbiased case, where x_1 and x_2 are random integer variables uniformly distributed between 1 and 6; the probabilities of the individual input values are shown in square parentheses.*

	x_1 = 1 [1/6]	x_1 = 2 [1/6]	x_1 = 3 [1/6]	x_1 = 4 [1/6]	x_1 = 5 [1/6]	x_1 = 6 [1/6]
x_2 = 1 [1/6]	1/36	1/36	1/36	1/36	1/36	1/36
x_2 = 2 [1/6]	1/36	1/36	1/36	1/36	1/36	1/36
x_2 = 3 [1/6]	1/36	1/36	1/36	1/36	1/36	1/36
x_2 = 4 [1/6]	1/36	1/36	1/36	1/36	1/36	1/36
x_2 = 5 [1/6]	1/36	1/36	1/36	1/36	1/36	1/36
x_2 = 6 [1/6]	1/36	1/36	1/36	1/36	1/36	1/36

Example B.2 (opposite) shows that there are no short-cut formulae for choosing input events to obtain an output event of desired rarity – even for the simple case of summing two independent and identically distributed variables. In particular, the example shows that the product of the rarities of the input events does not define the rarity of the resultant output event. In general, the product of the input rarities overestimates the resultant output rarity. A corollary of this false approach is that design values of the output variable will be underestimated.

Some terminology

The probabilities written along the top, and down the side, of the matrix in Table B.3 define the probability density function of x_1 and x_2 respectively. These are often referred to as the ***marginal density functions***. The matrix of probabilities itself defines the ***joint density function*** of x_1 and x_2. Note that the column-sums of the matrix of probabilities make up the marginal density function of x_1, and the row-sums make up the marginal density function of x_2. In the above example, the marginal density functions are identical and uniform, with probabilities [1/6, 1/6, 1/6, 1/6, 1/6, 1/6].

The throw of two interdependent dice

Example B.3 illustrates that the effect of dependence – here defined as the tendency for critical values of the input variables to occur together – is to increase the frequency with which a given extreme magnitude of the output variable is experienced. This means that dependence increases the magnitude of the output

---

Example B.2 Erroneous multiplication of input-event rarities: 1-in-12 maximum score for a dice pair

It is sometimes mistakenly thought that input events of 1-in-T_1 and 1-in-T_2 rarities can be combined to obtain an output event of 1-in-$T_1 T_2$ rarity.

A convenient factorisation of 1/12 is:

$$1/12 = (1/6).(1/2)$$

The 1-in-6 maximum score from one die is 6, because one out of six throws is expected to be greater or equal to 6. The 1-in-2 maximum score is 4, because one in two throws (or three in six) will typically be greater or equal to 4. Thus, summing the 1-in-6 and 1-in-2 maximum scores for the individual dice yields a score of 10. This is less than the 1-in-12 maximum score for the throw of a dice pair, which Example B.1 shows to be 11.

Another factorisation is:

$$1/12 = (1/4).(1/3)$$

The 1-in-3 maximum score from one die is 5, because two out of six throws score 5 or more. A 1-in-6 maximum score is 6. The 1-in-4 maximum score can be thought of as 5½, since 1-in-4 (i.e. 3/12) is intermediate to 1-in-3 (i.e. 4/12) and 1-in-6 (i.e. 2/12). Thus, summing the 1-in-4 and 1-in-3 maximum scores yields 10½. Again, this result is less than the 1-in-12 maximum score for the dice pair.

It transpires that the 1-in-12 maximum score of 11 could be synthesised by summing the 1-in-3 maximum event for one die and the 1-in-6 maximum event for the other. This conclusion is reached by considering all the combinations. Note that the product of the input rarities (1-in-3 and 1-in-6) overestimates the resultant output rarity (i.e. yielding 1-in-18 rather than 1-in-12).

Even in cases where a particular combination of input rarities can be found that yields the required output rarity, the approach is still flawed. This is simply demonstrated. In the above example, the die throws, x_1 and x_2, are identically distributed. The dice are therefore interchangeable, and there is no justification for synthesising the extreme event from the dice pair in a manner that attaches greater importance to one die than the other.

---

variable of a given rarity. If the dependence structure is known, and there are no additional complications (such as serial dependence in the input values), the risk assessment proceeds as in the independent case; but these are two big *if*'s in practical problems.

B.3   How flooding problems differ from dice problems

B.3.1 Setting up the joint probability problem

The first task is to choose an output variable to represent the critical *effect*. In the dice problem (Section B.2), the effect – a high score – is represented directly and unequivocally. In a flooding problem, the output variable is often the maximum

---

Example B.3 What is the risk of scoring 11 or more with unbiased but interdependent dice, in which the two die scores never differ by more than one?

The first step is to determine the matrix of probabilities (Table B.4). In this case, the matrix is tridiagonal rather than uniform (contrast with Table B.3). The problem is again solved by considering all the possible outcomes. As before:

$$Pr(y \geq 11) = Pr(y = 11) + Pr(y = 12)$$
$$= Pr(x_1 = 6 \ \& \ x_2 = 5) + Pr(x_1 = 5 \ \& \ x_2 = 6) + Pr(x_1 = 6 \ \& \ x_2 = 6)$$

However, for the interdependent dice pair, this yields:

$$Pr(y \geq 11) = 1/18 + 1/18 + 2/18 = 2/9$$

Thus, a combined score of 11 is now a much more frequent event than in the independent case, with a risk of 2/9 rather than 1/12.

Note that evaluation of the 2-in-9 (i.e. 8-in-36) maximum event involves just the three highlighted elements of the matrix in Table B.4, whereas it involves eight or more elements in the independent case. From Table B.3, the 2-in-9 maximum event in the independent case can be assessed to be a score of 9½. This illustrates that the effect of dependence is to concentrate the probability of occurrence into particular parts of the matrix of output values.

Table B.4 *Matrix of probabilities: a dependent but unbiased case, where x_1 and x_2 are integer variables uniformly distributed between 1 and 6 but are constrained to differ by no more than one*

	$x_1 = 1$	$x_1 = 2$	$x_1 = 3$	$x_1 = 4$	$x_1 = 5$	$x_1 = 6$
$x_2 = 1$	2/18	1/18	0	0	0	0
$x_2 = 2$	1/18	1/18	1/18	0	0	0
$x_2 = 3$	0	1/18	1/18	1/18	0	0
$x_2 = 4$	0	0	1/18	1/18	1/18	0
$x_2 = 5$	0	0	0	1/18	1/18	1/18
$x_2 = 6$	0	0	0	0	1/18	2/18

water level, which acts as a surrogate for the undesired effect (e.g. inundation of property).

The input variables are chosen to represent the **causes** of the undesired event. In the dice problem, the causes of the extreme output value are fully specified by the input variables (i.e. the individual die scores). The causes of a flooding problem are, in contrast, difficult to specify precisely. In a fluvial-tidal reach, the peak magnitudes of the river flow and sea level are clearly important – but so too are the shapes of the fluvial and tidal hydrographs, and the relative timing of their peaks.

If a joint probability analysis is to be feasible, it is necessary to represent the causes of the flood within a small number of summary variables. For some fluvial-tidal problems on slowly responding catchments, Jones (1998) suggests that the 6-hour mean river flow and the 6-hour maximum sea level can suffice as the primary input variables. The choice of six hours reflects the time over which most UK tidal basins alternately fill and empty. Jones refers to this as ***time-blocking***; the formal input and output variables represent summaries of more complicated behaviour within time-blocks (see §B.3.5). Some exploratory analysis may be necessary to understand the prototype system before choosing the input variables. A particular concern is to ensure that the chosen inputs adequately represent all the situations under which an extreme output value can occur. However, compromises may be necessary to match the study to the type of data available for analysis.

B.3.2 Structure functions and system models

Consider a joint probability problem in which an extreme value of the output variable, y, arises if one or both of two input variables, x_1 and x_2, are high. As in all joint probability methods, it is necessary to know or develop a model that represents the relationship that the output variable takes to the input variables. This is the structure function:

$$y = f(x_1, x_2) \tag{B.1}$$

In the dice problems (§B.2), the structure function provides an exact model of the system: $y = x_1 + x_2$. In flooding problems, the structure function has to relate the **chosen** output variable to the **chosen** input variables, as emphasised by Ibidapo-Obe and Beran (1988). A detailed model of the prototype system – e.g. of time-varying flows and water levels in a fluvial-tidal reach – is not itself the structure function. Occasionally, the structure function may be derived by regression modelling using direct measurements from the prototype system. However, this approach will be sensitive to the particular sample of triplets (x_1, x_2, y) observed, and may not extrapolate satisfactorily to more extreme events. More typically, the structure function is derived by regression analysis of results obtained from extensive runs of a hydraulic model. In fluvial-tidal problems, the system model may be a trusted computational model of the entire reach: from the (fluvial) section where river flows are measured to the (tidal) section at which sea levels are measured or can be inferred. In other cases, a scaled model in a hydraulics laboratory may be used. It is possible to extend the structure function formulation (Equation B.1) by including an error term to allow for the fact that an exact relationship does not hold.

An example of a structure function for a fluvial-tidal problem is given in Figure B.1. The lines indicate maximum water level at a site subject to fluvial-tidal influence. The levels are conditional on a given peak sea-level x_1 and daily mean river-flow x_2 and derive from a computational hydraulic model of the tidal Thames. The diagram also shows paired observations of the input variables (x_1, x_2).

B.3.3 Failure regions

It is instructive to plot the structure function for the threshold value of y corresponding to failure (see Figure B.2). Combinations of input values that yield an output value greater than the critical threshold define the ***failure region***.

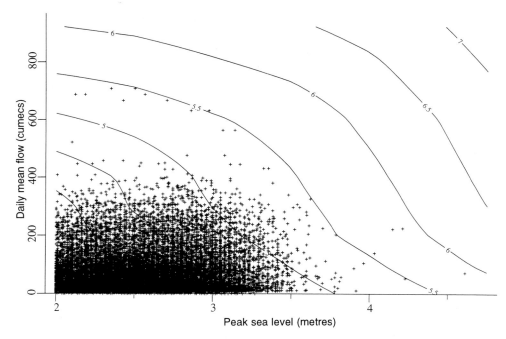

Figure B.1 *Structure function for peak water-level (m) at Eel Pie Island, London, conditional on peak sea-level (m) at Southend and daily mean river-flow (m³ s⁻¹) at Teddington; paired observations of sea level and river flow are also shown.*

The structure function is a summary model that relates the output variable to the input variables **chosen** for use in the joint probability analysis. It will often derive from a detailed model of the prototype system: perhaps, one formulated and calibrated in a prior study.

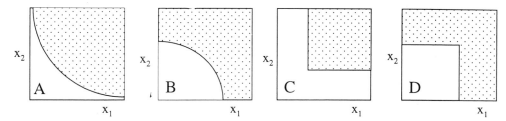

Figure B.2 *Shapes of failure regions: in the shaded zone, paired inputs precipitate failure (adapted from Coles and Tawn, 1994)*

Cases A and B are perhaps most typical of joint probability problems in flood estimation. In Case A, failure occurs readily if both variables are moderately extreme, so any dependence between the variable is likely to be influential. Dependence is likely to be less important in Case B, where failure arises if either variable is sufficiently extreme. Cases C and D represent exceptional situations. Dependence would be highly influential and damaging in Case C, where an extreme value of both variables is required to trigger failure. In Case D, an extreme value of x_1 or x_2 always precipitates failure; in this situation, intervariable dependence would beneficially reduce the frequency with which failures occur.

B.3.4 Event definition

Interest in extremes

In dice problems, it is reasonable to consider all the possible values of the input variables. The extreme values are essentially of similar character to the main body of values, only higher. The throw of a five or six does not demand any special treatment in the analysis. Flooding problems present several differences. First, the input variables can take a very wide range of values, many of which are ordinary while only a few are extreme. There is particular interest in the few extreme values, and in their individual magnitudes.

The interest in extremes leads naturally to extreme value analyses, in which all independent events above a threshold are examined (see Volume 3). Annual maximum analysis is less suitable in joint probability problems, because annual maxima of the input variables often come from entirely different (i.e. non-concurrent) events. An exception may lie in some confluence problems where there is strong dependence between the input variables. More generally, a type of peaks-over-threshold (POT) approach to defining independent extreme events is needed.

Ordering and serial independence

Ordering and serial independence are central concepts in the analysis of extremes. In the univariate case, the POT events are **ordered** by the magnitude of the variable of interest, often the instantaneous peak value. In joint probability problems, the events are ordered by reference to the structure function. The ordering cannot be made from the input data alone, since this would not reflect features arising from their interaction.

In the dice example, each observation is **serially independent**: there is no carry-over or memory effect. This is not the case with most environmental data, and serial dependence in hourly rainfall, river-flow and tidal data complicates the interpretation of the frequency of extreme values. In the univariate case, it is possible to apply relatively simple criteria to ensure that POT events selected for analysis are (serially) independent (see **3** 23).

Defining independent events is less straightforward in the multivariate case. Consider that both tributaries in a confluence flood estimation problem respond to an intense storm, and that the flood peaks arrive at different times. In consequence, they yield a sustained high flow, rather than an extreme flood, at the subject site. How is this to be represented in the joint probability analysis? One possibility is to use three input variables: two primary variables defining the peak (e.g. 3-hour) flows on each tributary, and a secondary variable defining their relative arrival times at the confluence. In this example, it is possible to turn to rainfall data to confirm that the tributary floods are associated with the same meteorological event. A minor complication is that the secondary variable is undefined when a flood occurs on only one tributary. Fluvial-tidal flood problems give rise to somewhat different considerations, principally because one of the input variables (sea level) is periodic.

B.3.5 Time-blocking

For flood estimation at river sections where the tidal influence is strong, it is often known that peak water levels occur close to high tide. Along most of the UK shoreline, high tides have a dominant periodicity of 12.4 hours.

Ibidapo-Obe and Beran (1988), and Jones (1998), suggest that fluvial-tidal problems can often be treated by allowing one potential flood event per high tide. Flood events defined under this arrangement can in many cases be deemed to be serially independent. It is then possible to infer the frequency of an event in terms of the mean number of times per year that the condition is exceeded, there being about 705 potential events (i.e. high tides) per year. On slowly responding river systems, or where drainage from the river reach is constrained by gates or barriers, flood events may extend over two or more high tides, complicating the definition of serially independent events (e.g. see Thompson and Law, 1983).

Although also useful in other approaches (e.g. §B.5.4), the concept of time-blocking is particularly helpful when applying the double matrix method to fluvial-tidal problems. This is illustrated next. Section B.6 points to more advanced methods based on the analysis of multivariate extremes (e.g. Coles and Tawn, 1994).

B.4   Summary of the double matrix method

The double matrix method is summarised, with brief reference to steps in the solution of a fluvial-tidal flood estimation problem. ***The presentation is not definitive and should not be interpreted as a recommendation to use the method.*** The discussion reveals facets of joint probability problems that are also relevant when seeking to apply more formal statistical treatments (see §B.6).

B.4.1 Choosing the output variable and the input variables

The first task is to set up the joint probability problem, by choosing the output and input variables (Example B.4a).

Example B.4a   Setting up the problem

Consider as an example a fluvial-tidal problem for which 20 years of concurrent river flow and sea level data are available at hourly interval. The peak water level at the subject site is taken as the output variable. Using the time-blocking approach of Jones (1998), the input variables are taken as the 6-hour mean river flow and the 6-hour maximum sea level. A 20-year record yields 20 x 365¼ x 24/12.4 = 14139   6-hour periods centred on tidal peaks.

B.4.2 Converting from continuous to discrete variables

In flood problems, x_1, x_2 and y will usually be continuous variables, capable of taking any value, or any non-negative value. To invoke the double matrix method the input variables are first converted from continuous to discrete form. The simplest approach is to represent x_1 by its ***empirical density function***, i.e. the distribution of values observed in the data sample. This can be formed by choosing regular class intervals on x_1, e.g. allocating all river flows between 0.5 and 1.5 $m^3 s^{-1}$ to one interval (to which a value of 1 $m^3 s^{-1}$ can be assigned), all values between 1.5 and 2.5 $m^3 s^{-1}$ to the next interval, and so on. However, it can be advantageous to

---

Example B.4b   Evaluating the marginal density function via the cumulative distribution

The 6-hour mean river flow that is exceeded in 0.01% of high-tide periods can be estimated directly from the data, as a weighted average of the largest and 2nd largest values, since 14 139/10 000 = 1.4. Percentage points of the remainder of the (cumulative) distribution function can be obtained in similar fashion; for example, the 14th largest value provides an estimate of the value exceeded in 0.10% of high tides, since 14 139×10/10 000 ≈ 14. The marginal density functions thus derived have irregular class intervals but observations in each interval are equiprobable, with a probability of 0.0001. The same procedure can be used to obtain percentage points of the empirical distribution of tidal peaks.

---

transform the data whilst forming the marginal density function.

For illustrative purposes, Example B.4b transforms the marginal densities to a discrete uniform distribution, so that observations in each class interval are equiprobable. This sustains the analogy with die throws. In some joint probability problems, the relative importance of the input variables is initially unclear. Transforming the marginal density functions to uniform has the benefit of bringing the input variables to a common base, helping to avoid preconceptions.

A technique such as ***kernel density estimation*** (e.g. Scott, 1992) can be used to smooth the empirical density function. This is a ***distribution-free*** method, in the sense that it avoids making a specific assumption that the variable follows a particular type of distribution.

Optionally, a theoretical distribution, such as the Normal or Log-Normal distribution, can be fitted as part of the process of converting the input variables to discrete form. In addition to smoothing the marginal density function, this assists in representing input values more extreme than sampled in the dataset. Coles and Tawn (1994) transform the input variables to a unit Frechet distribution in a more formal approach than the double matrix method (see §B.6).

B.4.3 Setting up the matrix of probabilities

The matrix of probabilities can be based either on the empirical joint density function, or on an assumed or fitted theoretical model. Unlike the marginal density functions, derivation of the joint density demands concurrent records of the input variables (see Example B.4c).

Example B.4c   A fluvial-tidal problem: setting up the matrix of probabilities empirically

The percentage points of the cumulative distribution of x_1 are used to define class intervals to run across the top of the matrix. Those for x_2 define class intervals to run down the side. This defines a 100 x 100 matrix or a 10 000 x 10 000 matrix, according to whether whole percentage points or 0.01% points have been used. Paired observations (x_1, x_2) in the common period of record are assigned to cells of the matrix and a joint frequency histogram constructed. The empirical joint density function is then obtained by dividing the counts by the total number of paired observations.

If it can be shown that the input variables act independently, the matrix of probabilities can be compiled very much more easily: by simply multiplying the marginal probabilities (see §B.4.8). This must not be confused with the erroneous multiplication of input-event rarities (recall Example B.2).

B.4.4 Setting up the matrix of output values

The matrix of output values is set up by applying the structure function (see §B.3.2) to each combination of input values. In practice, attention can focus on those paired values of x_1 and x_2 that yield a y value near to the threshold of interest (see §B.3.3), avoiding the need to set out the whole matrix. The requirement is to distinguish those pairs (x_1, x_2) which yield y values greater than the threshold from those which do not.

B.4.5 Assessing inter-variable dependence

Dependence is a tendency for potentially critical values of the input variables to occur together more frequently than by chance alone. The opposite tendency can be termed ***counter-dependence***.

A natural way to check for dependence is a scatter-plot of the input variables, using paired values (x_1, x_2) drawn from the common period of record. The correlation coefficient provides a simple measure of dependence. For some structure functions, the failure region is such that extreme values of the output variable are typically triggered by an extreme value of one input variable only (e.g. Case B in Figure B.2). In such situations, the ordinary correlation coefficient may be something of a blunt instrument. First, its value will be influenced by the transformations chosen for the input variables. Second, the correlation coefficient evaluated over all observations provides a very broad measure of association whereas the feature influencing the extremal behaviour of the output variable may be the degree of dependence when one or both input variables is extreme. The correlation derived for variables transformed to uniform marginal distributions is equivalent to the Spearman rank correlation.

B.4.6 Evaluating the distribution of output values

In principle, the output value that is exceeded with a given frequency can be evaluated in the same way as for the dice examples, ***irrespective of whether the input variables are independent or dependent***. Elements in the matrix of output values are counted in descending order of magnitude, accumulating the probabilities of occurrence along the way, until a value of y is found that is exceeded with the required frequency. The process is repeated for different target frequencies, and the relevant section of the frequency distribution of the output variable derived. In practice, only the extreme part of the distribution is of interest.

Unfortunately, this is not quite the final answer. The frequencies have to be converted from exceedance probabilities in the total distribution of y values to exceedance probabilities in the distribution of extremes, most usually to annual exceedance probabilities (see Section A.1). Determining an appropriate frequency adjustment is not straightforward. This reflects fundamental difficulties in solving joint probability problems: (i) the identification of (serially) independent events and (ii) the precise definition of the input values associated with a given output event. Problems can sometimes be compounded by important seasonal effects.

B.4.7 Inferring the distribution of extreme output values

In order to infer the distribution of *extreme* output values from the distribution of *all* output values, it is necessary to know or specify the *rate of occurrence* of independent output events. In a slowly responding catchment such as the Thames at Kingston (39001), high river flows are sustained for many days, and there is scope for only about 50 independent events per year. In practice, this is reduced further by seasonal effects associated with groundwater and soil moisture conditions. In contrast, on a quickly responding catchment such as the Beverley Brook at Wimbledon (39005), flood events last for only a few hours. Thus, there is scope for several thousand independent events per year and, on such a heavily urbanised catchment, the flood potential is ever-present. These are relatively extreme examples. Nevertheless, in joint probability problems that seek to estimate flood frequency at a confluence – even of tributaries with similar response characteristics – the rate of occurrence of independent output events is known only rather approximately. For example, if the rate is known only to within a factor of five, flood frequency at the confluence will be known only to within a factor of about five. This is a very considerable drawback.

The derivation of an appropriate *frequency adjustment factor* is less problematic for fluvial-tidal flood estimation problems, if it is known that a flood can occur in any high-tide period but not otherwise. For most UK estuaries, there are about 705 high tides per year. It is then possible to convert non-exceedance probabilities in the double matrix method into non-exceedance probabilities per year by taking the 705th power. On this basis, the 50-year extreme corresponds to a non-exceedance probability of $0.98^{1/705} = 0.99997$ in the full distribution of output values.

In practice, application of the double matrix method typically requires extensive computations but meets no fundamental obstacle. The main concerns about the approach are:

- Whether the choice of input variables is too restrictive;

- Whether the final frequency adjustment is simplistic;

- Whether the method adequately exploits what is known about the extremal behaviour of the input variables.

B.4.8 Additional considerations: the independent case

Where the correlation coefficient (or the rank correlation) between input values is not significantly different from zero, it is reasonable to assume that the input variables act independently. Rather than using the empirical values, the matrix of probabilities (representing the joint density function) can be populated by the product of the marginal probabilities. This has the important advantage of allowing use of best estimates of the marginal density functions, rather than those based only on paired observations (x_1, x_2). If the input variables have been transformed to uniform, the matrix of probabilities will be uniform, imitating the matrix in the independent dice example (see Table B.3).

Where the input variables can be shown to act independently, it may be practical to allow the refinement of introducing a secondary variable that represents the relative timing of the two primary inputs (e.g. Thompson and Law, 1983). This adds a third dimension to the matrices (of output values and probabilities) in the double matrix method, but does not fundamentally alter the solution method.

B.4.9 Additional considerations: the dependent case

Where there is significant correlation, it is necessary to estimate the bivariate density function for x_1 and x_2. If extensive concurrent records are available, the empirical joint density can be used, as in Example B.4c. Otherwise, it may be necessary to select and fit a theoretical model. These are specialised tasks, requiring considerable statistical expertise.

In some applications, there may be little alternative but to adopt the joint density function derived in some earlier study of a similar flooding problem blessed with extensive records. That such an assumption may be implausible can be illustrated for joint probability studies of coastal flooding. Once account is taken of shoreline bathymetry and exposure, the phenomena giving rise to storm surge and wave attack – principally, low-pressure weather systems – are likely to make the degree of dependence between surge and waves highly site-specific.

The uncertainty of assumptions about inter-variable dependence – and the typical sensitivity of results to the assumption made (e.g. Anderson *et al.*, 1994) – highlight a further underlying difficulty of solving joint probability problems. The degree of dependence between the input variables can usually only be judged from the analysis of concurrent records. Typically, these record lengths are relatively short in comparison to the target return period for which flood estimates are required. Results are likely to be highly sensitive to the chance occurrence (or non-occurrence) of one or two extreme events in the period of record in which the input variables are jointly extreme.

B.5   Avoiding joint probability problems

Because their solution is difficult, and not always convincing, joint probability problems are worth avoiding. Where possible, it is usually preferable to carry out the extreme value analysis directly on the variable of interest, e.g. water level at the subject site. There are several possibilities.

B.5.1 Direct analysis of output variable

A long-term record of the relevant variable is the ideal. It is worth checking for any gauged records close to the subject site.

B.5.2 Continuous simulation of output variable

An emerging approach to flood frequency estimation is to use hydrological and/or hydraulic models to simulate the variable of interest continuously (see §9.6) based on observed input data. The simulated record is then analysed as if it had been observed. The approach has much to commend it as a way of avoiding joint probability problems. However, it is necessary to have concurrent long-term records of the relevant input variables, and a trustworthy system model.

For water-level estimation in a tidal river, the ideal would be to have long-term hourly records of sea level in the estuary and river flow above the tidal limit. For water level estimation at a confluence, tributary flow records are needed. In either case, it is possible to consider using hydrological models to simulate river flow from long-term rainfall records. In the confluence problem, it would be important to use rainfall records from different gauges when synthesising river flows on the two tributaries; otherwise, their simulated hydrographs will be unnaturally similar.

Where the input variables are known to act independently, stochastic models (e.g. Metcalfe, 1997) can be used to generate long-term data series for one or both input variables. Techniques for generating time-series data for interdependent variables are, however, not yet well established.

B.5.3 Episodic simulation of output variable

A variant on the above approach is to restrict the simulation to those periods when an extreme value of the output variable is possible. Thus, for water-level estimation in a tidal river, simulations would be carried out only if river flow or sea level is conducive to an extreme event. This reduces the data extraction and computational tasks.

B.5.4 Historical emulation

There are variously named methods – e.g. ***trigger functions*** (Reed, 1992) and ***direct hindcasting*** (Hawkes and Hague, 1994) – which avoid both continuous simulation and an explicit joint probability analysis. Coles and Tawn (1994) refer to the ***univariate structure variable approach*** whereas Jones (1998) refers to ***historical emulation***.

Rather than using the system model to simulate the output variable continuously, the historical emulation method initially formulates the problem in a similar way to the double matrix method (see Section B.4). Input and output variables are chosen and time-blocked (see §B.3.5), and the structure function is derived based on extensive trials with the system model. The method differs from the double matrix method by applying the structure function model to potential flood events drawn from the historical period of record, and uses it to construct a series of extreme output values. These are then subjected to a classical univariate analysis.

In essence, the approach reduces the dimensionality of the estimation problem by specifying a formula that summarises the way that the input variables combine to influence the output variable. This is, of course, the structure function (§B.3.2). The structure function model is applied throughout the period of concurrent record, either continuously or episodically, to provide a series of output values. A classical univariate extreme value analysis is then undertaken. R.L. Smith (discussion to Coles and Tawn, 1994 and *pers. comm.*) points out that this approach is wasteful when the input variables are independent. This is because use of the structure function gives precedence to particular ***paired*** values of (x_1, x_2) that have occurred, when none is warranted. Put another way, the amount of information available when analysing the set of single values $f(x_1, x_2)$ is reduced compared to that in the full set of data.

The historical emulation method is relatively straightforward to apply, and makes effective use of available data and resources. It is at its most useful when understanding of the prototype system allows a confident choice of input and output variables, and provides a well-defined structure function.

B.6 Further guidance

This appendix has introduced some of the principles and pitfalls of solving joint probability problems. The double matrix method (Sections B.2 and B.4) provides a relatively understandable solution approach if the input variables are independent. However, there can be uncertainty in interpreting the frequency of the extreme

Overview

output values (see §B.4.7). Approaches based on continuous simulation (§B.5.2) and historical emulation (§B.5.4) are also worth considering.

More formal statistical methods for solving joint probability problems have been developed. Coles and Tawn (1994) present a ***multivariate extreme method***, which can be thought of as a considerable extension to, and formalisation of, the double matrix method. One of the particular strengths of the multivariate extreme method is that it is able to exploit best estimates of the extremal behaviour of the input variables, rather than being limited to that judged from the period of common record. Thus, solution of a fluvial-tidal problem could use considered estimates of river flood frequency (e.g. by FEH Volume 3) and extreme sea level (e.g. by Dixon and Tawn, 1994). The multivariate extreme method has also been applied to reservoir flood safety assessment (Anderson and Nadarajah, 1993; Anderson *et al.*, 1994). A feature of the approach is to distinguish primary and secondary input variables (Reed and Anderson, 1992). The secondary variables – such as antecedent reservoir level and wind direction – have an important influence but do not in themselves create the extreme output value. The approach allows due account to be taken of the secondary variables without increasing the dimensionality of the joint probability problem.

The drawback of the multivariate extreme method is that it is highly specialised, and is not yet fully insulated from the difficulties of defining extreme events discussed in §B.3.4. However, Coles and Tawn (1994) point to a potentially redeeming advantage of explicitly multivariate approaches compared to univariate methods such as those summarised in Section B.5. The latter suffer the drawback that there is little information to help with the selection of an appropriate extreme value distribution to aid extrapolation to long return periods – a serious consideration when the output variable is known to reflect a combination of input factors. Coles and Tawn suggest that the simpler methods are more likely to lead to underestimation of extreme values than to overestimation.

Jones (1998) provides further guidance on the solution of joint probability problems, and presents a detailed case study of flood design in fluvial-tidal reaches of the Thames. Jones demonstrates how a structure function approach can be modified to take account of tidal barrier operation; a further problem is to assess the uncertainty arising from the need to base barrier-closure decisions on *forecast* sea level.

In some joint probability problems, there can be a concern that inter-dependence in the primary input variables may intensify in the most extreme weather conditions: for example, in exceptionally sustained wet spells. Specific ways of indexing inter-variable dependence in extreme values can be based on the concept of an ***effective number of independent variables***. This is analogous to the effective number of independent sites used by Dales and Reed (1989) and the extremal coefficient used by Coles and Tawn (1994). Although Coles and Tawn promote its wider use, the concept of an effective number of independent variables is more convincing, and less site-specific, when the input variables are of the same kind: e.g. two river flows in flood frequency estimation at a confluence. Reed and Dwyer (1996) attempt to relate extremal behaviour of the output variable directly to extremal behaviour of the input variables, without reference to a system model. This would appear to be simplistic. However, their attempted short-cut approach might be revisited once experience has been gained of many joint probability problems of a given type.

Appendix C   Augmenting flood estimates by historical review

C.1   Why carry out a historical review?

There are several reasons why it is helpful to augment a flood frequency analysis by examining evidence of floods prior to the period of gauged record. Most studies call for estimation of the magnitude of infrequent floods: for example, the so-called 100-year flood. This is the flood peak having a probability of 0.01 of being exceeded in any year. Such a flood is not certain to have occurred within the gauged period. For example, there is only an even chance of having experienced the 100-year flood at least once within a 69-year period. This is verified by substituting $T = 100$ and $M = 69$ in the **risk equation** (see §A.2)

$$r = 1 - (1 - 1/T)^M \qquad\qquad (C.1)$$

where r is the risk (i.e. the probability) of experiencing one or more exceedances of the T-year flood in an M-year period ($0 \leq r \leq 1$).

Return period

It is important to think clearly when using the term return period. There is no regularity in flood occurrences. A very long period may elapse without an extreme event occurring. The occurrence of an extreme flood does not make a further extreme flood any more or less likely to occur. However, it may lead to a change in perceptions and estimates of flood risk.

A small sample

Attention inevitably focuses on the largest floods in the period of gauged record. Floods in March 1968, January 1982, February 1991 and February 1995 were large enough to have a significant general impact on communities vulnerable to flooding from the River Ure in North Yorkshire. In this example, deductions about the 100-year flood inevitably pivot on the peak flows recorded in these four floods. Yet four numbers represent a very small sample. One would not be confident in judging the height characteristics of drainage engineers – is there natural selection? – by sampling the first four in a membership list. The average of a sample of four might provide a reasonable estimate, but it might not. Given the natural variability of climate, it is not unusual for a gauging station to have experienced no major flood, even in a 20 or 30-year period of record. Thus, the first reason why a historical review is helpful is that the gauged sample of major floods is usually very small.

An unusual sample?

Particular concern arises when a community has experienced a sequence of floods. There is undoubtedly an element of misfortune in experiencing four major floods within 30 years (on the Ure at Boroughbridge, see above) or two within a calendar

year (on the Kenwyn at Truro in 1988). Another view is that there may be some factor leading to major floods becoming more frequent, either generally or in the particular river basin. Climate change, urbanisation and drainage works are the factors most often mentioned. A historical review can help to put recent flood experiences into a longer-term perspective (Acreman and Horrocks, 1990). A *flood-rich* period (Grew and Werritty, 1995) will stimulate public calls for flood risk to be ameliorated. Just as significantly, residents and planners may lose sight of vulnerabilities in consequence of a *flood-poor* period.

Uncovering forgotten information

In addition to putting the statistical analysis of floods into a longer-term perspective, uncovering forgotten information adds credibility to an investigation, and contributes to the public understanding of flood risk. Knowledge that a comparable or worse flood has occurred previously can be a very valuable piece of information in the aftermath of a major flood, encouraging public debate to focus on assessing risk rather than apportioning blame.

C.2 Sources of historical information

Historical information about floods is often given in earlier studies of a flooding problem. Various additional sources of information can be explored, including:

- Abstraction of heavy-rainfall dates and data from: long-term rainfall records; *British Rainfall* yearbooks; periodicals with a particular UK emphasis such as *Meteorological Magazine* (and its predecessor *Symons's Monthly Meteorological Magazine*), *Weather* and the less-formal-than-it-sounds *Journal of Meteorology*; and the *Climate Observers Link*;

- Searches of documents held in public libraries: local, district and regional;

- Inspection of newspaper records for specific dates when – judged from other evidence – floods may have occurred;

- Additional compilations and sources suggested by Potter (1978) and Jones *et al.* (1984).

Reports found often refer to earlier extreme events. A new source of information is the British Hydrological Society *Chronology of British Hydrological Events*, with the World Wide Web address: ***http://www.dundee.ac.uk/geography/cbhe***.

"*Land of Singing Waters*" (Archer, 1992) comprises a remarkable review of historical floods in north-east England, from the Tees northwards. Archer finds several 19th century compilations that give specific information on flood dates and levels in the region. The book is notable both for the richness of information gathered and the lucid intertwining of floods research and local history. In addition to the sources listed above, Archer considers flood-stones and flood-marks, diaries, parish registers and reports of County Quarter Sessions. The latter often record flood damage to important bridges (see Jervoise, 1930, 1931a, 1931b). Archer sets particular value on archive material gathered by catchment boards, river authorities and local authorities, such as notes of contemporary interviews with those who experienced or witnessed flooding.

Accounts of the impact of flooding are inevitably conditioned by what was considered exceptional at the time. The subjective account of a general diarist inevitably carries less weight than a referenced flood level quoted by an organisation with a defined interest in river levels. Local newspaper reports – except those written in sensational style – can perhaps be considered nearer to the latter in terms of reliability. However, it is worth checking subsequent issues for corrections and letters. Daily rainfall measurements are frequently quoted. Historical maps can in certain cases be highly informative, showing watercourse positions and (sometimes) explicitly labelling areas "liable to flood". The recent trend towards publication of books of local photographs of historical interest can provide another source of information.

The process of historical review is messy, and can be likened to solving a jigsaw for which an unknown number of pieces are missing, others are damaged, and some belong to a different puzzle. To keep subjectivity to a minimum, and facilitate checks, the sources of historical information should always be recorded. Where possible, original documents should be inspected.

In some localities there may be little information existing, and therefore little to find. But in as many cases, the principal difficulties will lie in determining a cost-effective strategy – for finding, organising and digesting information – and in inferring what the information reveals about flood frequency at the subject site. When there is a customer paying for an assessment of flood risk, historical review must strengthen or illuminate the flood frequency estimation rather than become a goal in itself.

C.3 Interpretation

C.3.1 Introduction

Historical information varies greatly from case to case. The review may yield important information about the typical character of the largest floods. It is helpful to uncover the proportion of events in which antecedent wetness or concurrent snowmelt was an influential factor on flood formation. Earlier flood-rich periods can be a pointer to the phases when flood risk has been a major issue, and the review can help to chart the evolution of both town development and flood defence.

Folklore

It is not uncommon for local opinion to assert that extreme floods are always/only triggered by a particular combination of conditions: for example, heavy rainfall with melting snow, heavy rainfall with a spring tide, or heavy rainfall when soils are hardened by drought. A historical review can help to broaden perceptions – or at least throw light on the origin of the belief.

In a historical review, two questions are often uppermost: "Has flood behaviour changed?" and "Can a tentative ranking of floods be constructed for a usefully long period such as the last 100 to 200 years?" The first question may be easy to answer if there have been major alterations to the floodplain, embankments, or channel constrictions, or if a major reservoir has been constructed within the catchment. If there is evidence of systematic change, it may be prudent to discard the historical flood data and to fall back on other methods (see Chapter 5). If the second challenge can be met, there is scope to take the analysis further, and to seek to reconcile the historical flood data with a flood frequency analysis of gauged data.

C.3.2 Formal methods

Based on research by Leese (1973), the Flood Studies Report (FSR) includes specific methods for combining gauged and historical flood data in a censored analysis of annual maxima (FSR **I**.2.8). In the ***historic flood-mark*** case, all floods rising above a known high threshold are thought to have been marked, and peak flow magnitudes have been estimated by a flow-level relationship. In the ***historic flood-date*** (or 'missing peaks') case, only the number of floods exceeding the high threshold is known.

A preliminary step in either situation is to infer the period of record over which historical floods have been noted. If, as is usual, the earliest-marked flood is large, a judgement has to be made of the prior date at which a lesser flood (but one greater than the chosen threshold) would have been marked, had it occurred. The easy option – of defining the period of historical record to begin on the day of the earliest-marked flood – leads to bias, since the sample period from which large floods are drawn cannot then be considered random. The difficulty is widespread because the first flood to be marked is usually one considered exceptional at the time: the proverbial "largest flood in living memory" or "flood of the century". This introduces the related bias that a flood of given level is more likely to be noted once a system of flood-marking has started. These features are a considerable disincentive to mechanistic incorporation of historical flood data.

Formal solutions to the two cases can be sought by iterative methods based on maximum likelihood estimation (see FSR **I**.1.3). However, the methods are reasonably specialised: varying according to the statistical distribution chosen to describe flood frequency. For some datasets and distributions, the iterative scheme may fail to converge.

C.3.3 Informal methods

The Handbook recommends a less formal approach to incorporating historical flood data. Some reasons for this have already been given. However, the principal reason for rejecting formal solutions is that the preferred estimate of flood frequency – with which the historical data are to be reconciled – is itself likely to be based on a combination of methods. Often, the preferred estimate will be based on flood peak data pooled from several sites. In other cases, the preferred estimate may combine statistical and rainfall-runoff methods. Given the many possibilities indicated in Chapter 5, it is not thought practical at this time to develop formal procedures for incorporating historical flood data.

A more intuitive approach is therefore recommended, in which a preferred flood frequency curve is derived conventionally (see Chapter 5), and then reviewed in the light of the historical information. The largest historical floods are superposed on a plot of the preferred flood frequency curve, using the customary Gringorten plotting-position formula (see **3** 15.3.5). Where there is uncertainty about the historical flood magnitude, this can be indicated by sketching an interval about the plotted magnitude (see Figure C.1). Similarly, uncertainty about the length of period from which the extremes are drawn can be indicated by sketching an interval about the plotting position.

Particular care is recommended in cases when the historical flood data suggest that the preferred frequency curve is too high. Could the historical flood series be incomplete? Might the same flood level today represent a higher flow, because the effective floodplain has been reduced by embanking or infill?

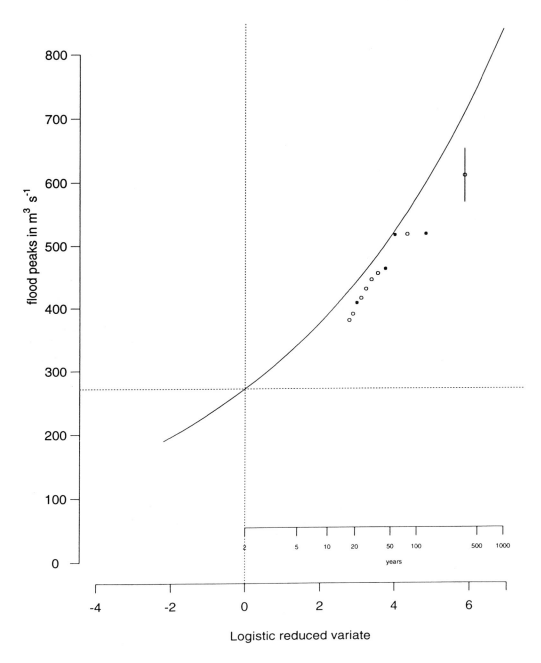

Figure C.1 *Informal incorporation of historical flood data: the flood frequency curve shown is a preferred estimate obtained without reference to historical data; the symbols denote the 12 largest floods in 200 years, plotted at Gringorten plotting positions; the solid symbols denote gauged estimates; the open symbols represent historical floods in estimated rank order but of unknown magnitude; an informal estimate of the highest flood is indicated by a vertical bar. In this example, the historical flood data do not suggest that the preferred flood frequency curve is an underestimate.*

Greater respect for historical flood data is recommended when they suggest that the preferred frequency curve may be too low. The fitted distribution should be adjusted in acknowledgement of the historical data. Where the preferred flood frequency curve is a 3-parameter statistical distribution such as the Generalised Logistic (see **3** 15.3), this might be done by increasing the L-skewness experimentally. However, a subjective sketched adjustment is possibly more honest. The position of an inflection in the sketched curve might be chosen to reflect the flood magnitude or return period at which floodplain storage is thought to begin, or cease, to have a major effect.

Being keener to allow estimates to be increased than reduced appears somewhat unscientific. However, the uneven treatment can be justified on two grounds. First, there is greater scope for the historical series to overlook the occurrence of a real flood than to accidentally include a false one. Second, in part because floods are bounded below (i.e. are non-negative), and – at least within the typical return-period range of interest – unbounded above, there is generally greater scope for underestimation than overestimation.

Appendix D Bibliography of related technical guidance

D.1 Introduction

The *Flood Estimation Handbook* is less comprehensive in subject coverage than, for example, *Australian Rainfall and Runoff* (Pilgrim, 1987). That text is notable in providing guidance in hydraulic calculations for the design of structures – including channels, culverts, embankments and bridge waterways – and in urban stormwater drainage design methods. Some texts that provide a UK perspective of these and other topics are now noted.

Most of the publications are textbooks or substantial technical reports that are relatively accessible. Scientific papers are listed only exceptionally, where they provide important practical guidance that is not available elsewhere.

When referring to these texts it is, of course, important to keep in mind that some of them use (or cite) methods of rainfall and frequency estimation that pre-date the *Flood Estimation Handbook*.

Listings

For brevity, publications are listed where possible by series or institution. In this case, the author and date are given in square brackets. Other publications are grouped by topic and cited more conventionally.

D.2 Series and institutions

ADAS

RB 345 *The design of field drainage pipe systems*

BHS (British Hydrological Society, c/o ICE, 1 Great George Street, London)

Occasional Paper No. 7 *Palæohydrology: context, components and application.*
[ed. Branson, J., 1996]
Register of independent consultants.
Chronology of British Hydrological Events:
web site: *http://www.salford.ac/uk/civils/BHS/cbhe*

BRE Digests (Building Research Establishment, Garston, Watford)

365 *Soakaways* [1991]

BSI (British Standards Institution, London)

BS 6367 *Code of practice for drainage of roofs and paved areas* [1983]
BS 7843 *Guide to the acquisition and management of meteorological precipitation data* [1996]

BS 8005   *Code of practice for sewerage* [1987]
BS 8301   *Code of practice for building drainage* [1985]

CIRIA (Construction Industry Research and Information Association, London)

[B series available from Butterworth-Heinemann]

B14   *The design of flood storage reservoirs* [Hall, M.J., Hockin, D.L., Ellis, J.B., with contributions from Packman, J.C., 1993]
R123/4   *Scope for control of urban runoff* [1992]
R141   *Design of sewers to control sediment problems* [Ackers, J.C., Butler, D. and May, R.W.P., 1996]
R142   *Control of pollution from highway drainage discharges* [Luker, M. and Montague, K.N., 1994]
R156   *Infiltration drainage – manual of good practice* [Bettess, R., 1996]
R161   *Small embankment reservoirs* [Kennard, M.F., Hoskins, C.G. and Fletcher, M., 1996]
R168   *Culvert design manual* [Ramsbottom, D., Day, R. and Rickard, C., 1997]
TN123   *Engineering works and wetlands in lowland areas generally drained by gravity* [1986]
TN134   *Guide to the analysis of open-channel spillway flow* [Ellis, J.R., 1989]

DoE (Department of the Environment, London – now part of DETR)

Circ. 30/92   *Development and flood risk* [1992]
PPG12   *Development plans and regional planning guidance* [1992]

EA (Environment Agency, Bristol) Technical Reports (available from WRc)

          Policy and practice for the protection of floodplains [1997]
W109   *Fluvial design guide* [Binnie, Black and Veatch, 1998]

FWR (Foundation for Water Research, Marlow)

CL0009   *Urban pollution management (UPM) manual* [2nd edition, 1998]
          Linkage of flood frequency curve with maximum flood estimate. [Lowing, M.J., 1995]

HR Wallingford Reports (Hydraulics Research Wallingford Ltd, Wallingford)

SR331   *The hydraulics and hydrology of pumped drainage systems: an engineering guide* [Samuels, P.G., 1993]
SR490   *Handbook for assessment of hydraulic performance of environmental channels* [Fisher, K.R., 1996]

ICE publications (Institution of Civil Engineers, Thomas Telford Services Ltd, 1 Great George Street, London)

Floods and reservoir safety [3rd edition, 1996]
Land drainage and flood defence responsibilities [3rd edition, 1996]

IH Reports (Institute of Hydrology, Wallingford)

46   *The use of historic records for the augmentation of hydrological data* [Potter, H.R., 1978]

102   *Regional flood and storm hazard assessment* [Dales, M.Y. and Reed, D.W., 1989]

113   *Impact of improved land drainage on river flows* [Robinson, M., 1990]

114   *Reservoir flood estimation: another look* [Reed, D.W. and Field, E.K., 1992]

124   *Flood estimation for small catchments* [Marshall, D.C.W. and Bayliss, A.C., 1994]

126   *Hydrology of soil types: a hydrologically-based classification of the soils of the UK* [Boorman, D.B., Hollis, J.M. and Lilly, A., 1995]

130   *Flood risk map for England and Wales* [Morris, D.G. and Flavin, R.W., 1996]

IH/BGS Hydrological data UK (Institute of Hydrology and British Geological Survey, Wallingford)

Hydrometric register and statistics 1991-1995 [Marsh, T.J. and Lees, M.L., 1998]

IWEM (Institution of Water and Environmental Management, London)

Water Practice Manuals:

7   *River engineering – design principles* [ed. T.W. Brandon, 1987]

8   *River engineering – structures and coastal defence works* [ed. T.W. Brandon, 1989]

MAFF Publications (Ministry of Agriculture Fisheries and Food, London)

1214   *Flood and Coastal Defence: Project Appraisal Guidance Notes* [1993]
      To be superseded by:
      FCDPAG1 *Overview;* FCDPAG2 *Strategic Planning and Appraisal;*
      FCDPAG3 *Economic Appraisal;* FCDPAG4 *Risk Assessment;*
      FCDPAG5 *Environmental Appraisal;* FCDPAG6 *Post Project Evaluation*

1471   *Strategy for flood and coastal defence in England and Wales* [1993]

1793   *Water level management plans – a procedural guide for operating authorities* [Honnor, J. 1994]

Met. Office Hydrological Memoranda (Meteorological Office, Bracknell)

45   *The Meteorological Office rainfall and evaporation calculation system, MORECS* [Thompson, N., Barrie, I.A. and Ayles, M., 1981]

NRA R&D Notes (National Rivers Authority – now part of the Environment Agency, Bristol) [Available from WRc]

7   *Techniques for identification of floodplains* [Cole, J.A. and Sutcliffe, J.V., 1992]

471   *Pumping station design manual* [Bullen and Partners, 1995]

NWC (National Water Council, London)

Design and analysis of urban storm drainage – the Wallingford procedure [1981]

POL (Proudman Oceanographic Laboratory, Bidston, Birkenhead)

ID65   *Extreme sea-levels at the UK A-class sites: site-by-site analysis* [Dixon, M.J. and Tawn, J.A., 1994]

SEPA (Scottish Environment Protection Agency)

A guide to surface water best management practices [1996]
A guide to sustainable urban drainage [1997]

Scottish Office National Planning Policy Guidelines

7   *Planning and flooding* [1995]

TRRL (Transport and Road Research Laboratory, Crowthorne – now TRL)

CR2   *The drainage capacity of BS road gullies and a procedure for estimating their spacing* [1984]

WMO Operational Hydrology Reports (World Meteorological Organization)

1   *Manual for estimation of probable maximum precipitation* [1986]
30   *Hydrological aspects of combined effects of storm surges and heavy rainfall on river flow* [Ibidapo-Obe, O. and Beran, M.A., 1988]
33   *Statistical distributions for flood frequency analysis* [Cunnane, C., 1989]

WMO Publications (World Meteorological Organization, Geneva)

168   *Guide to hydrological practices: data acquisition and processing, analysis, forecasting and other applications* [5th edition, 1994]

WRc (Water Research centre, Swindon)

Sewers for adoption [4th edition, 1995]

D.3 Other publications

Climate change

Climate Change Impacts Review Group (1996) *Review of the potential effects of climate change in the UK.* HMSO.

Intergovernmental Panel on Climate Change (1996) *Climate change 1995: the IPCC scientific assessment.* [Eds J.T. Houghton, G.J. Jenkins and J.J.Ephraums] Cambridge University Press.

Ecology

Calow, P. and Petts, G.E. [eds] (1994) *The rivers handbook: hydrological and ecological principles.* Blackwell [two volumes].

Economics

Handmer, J. (1987) *Flood hazard management: British and international perspectives.* Short Run Press Ltd, Exeter.

N'Jai, A., Tapsell, S.M., Taylor, D., Thompson, P.M. and Witts, R.C. (1990) *FLAIR: Flood Loss Assessment Information Report.* Middlesex University Flood Hazard Research Centre.

Parker, D.J., Green, C.H. and Thompson, P.M. (1987) *Urban flood protection benefits: a project appraisal guide* [Red Manual]. Gower Technical Press, Aldershot.

Penning-Rowsell, E.C. and Chatterton, J.B. (1977) *The benefits of flood alleviation: a manual of assessment techniques* [Blue Manual]. Saxon House, Farnborough.

Flood events (specific)

Acreman, M.C. (1989) Hydrological analysis of the Truro floods of January and October 1988. *1988 Yearbook, Hydrological data UK*, IH/BGS, 27-33.

Anderson, M.G. and Calver, A. (1978) On the persistence of landscape fetures formed by a large flood. *Trans. Inst. British Geographers* **2**, 243-254. [Lynmouth flood revisited]

Archer, D.R. (1992) *Land of singing waters*. Spredden Press, Stocksfield, Northumbria. [Major study of historical floods in North-East England]

Black, A.R. and Anderson, J.L. (1994) The great Tay flood of January 1993. *1993 Yearbook, Hydrological data UK*, IH/BGS, 25-34.

Black, A.R. (1995) Regional flooding in Strathclyde, December 1994. *1994 Yearbook, Hydrological data UK*, IH/BGS, 29-34.

Bye, P. and Horner, M.J. (1998) *Easter 1998 floods*. Independent Review Team report to EA [two volumes].

Dobbie, C.H. and Wolf, P.O. (1953) The Lynmouth flood of August 1952. *Proc. ICE*, Part III, **2**, 522-588.

Frost, J.R. and Jones, E.C. (1989) The October 1987 flood on the River Twyi. *1987 Yearbook, Hydrological data UK*, IH/BGS, 23-29.

Hanwell, J.D. (1970) *The great storms and floods of July 1968 on Mendip*. Wessex Cave Club Occasional Publication Series 1, No.2, Pangbourne, 72pp.

Robinson, D.N. (1995) *The Louth flood of 29th May 1920*. Louth Naturalists' Antiquarian and Literary Society, Louth, Lincolnshire, 36pp.

Taylor, S.M. (1995) The Chichester flood, January 1994. *1994 Yearbook, Hydrological data UK*, IH/BGS, 23-27.

Flood warning

Collier, C.G. (1996) *Applications of weather radar systems: a guide to uses of radar data in meteorology and hydrology*. 2nd edition. John Wiley & Sons, Chichester.

Handmer, J. [ed.] (1997) *Flood warnings: issues and practice in total system design*. Flood Hazard Research Centre, Middlesex University.

Flood management

Penning-Rowsell, E.C. and Fordham, M. [Eds] (1994) *Floods across Europe: hazard assessment, modelling and management.* Middlesex University Press, London.

Flood routing

Price, R.K. (1985) Flood routing. In: *Developments in hydraulic engineering 3* [ed. P. Novak], Elsevier, 129-173.

Hydraulics

Chadwick, A. and Morfett, J. (1998) *Hydraulics in civil and environmental engineering.* 3rd edition. Spon, London.

HR Wallingford and Barr, D.I.H. (1998) *Tables for the hydraulic design of pipes, sewers and channels.* 7th edition [two volumes], Thomas Telford Ltd, London.

Knight, D.W. and Shiono, K. (1996) River channel and floodplain hydraulics. Chapter 5 in: *Floodplain processes.* (eds: M.G. Anderson, D.E. Walling and P.D. Bates), John Wiley & Sons Ltd., 139-181.

Novak, P. (1996) *Hydraulic structures.* 2nd edition, Spon, London, 1996.

Hydrology

Maidment, D.R. [ed.] (1992) *Handbook of Hydrology.* McGraw-Hill.

Shaw, E.M. (1989) *Engineering hydrology techniques in practice.* Ellis Horwood, Chichester.

Shaw, E.M. (1994) *Hydrology in practice.* 3rd edition, Chapman and Hall.

Smith, K. and Ward, R. (1998) *Floods: Physical processes and human impacts.* John Wiley & Sons.

Ward, R.C. and Robinson, M. (1999) *Principles of hydrology.* 4th edition, McGraw-Hill.

Wilson, E.M. (1990) *Engineering hydrology.* 4th edition. Macmillan.

Hydrometry

Herschy, R.W. (1995) *Streamflow measurement.* 2nd edition. Spon, London.

Herschy, R.W. [ed.] (1999) *Hydrometry: principles and practice.* 2nd edition. John Wiley & Sons, Chichester.

Risk

Adams, J. (1995) *Risk.* UCL Press Ltd, University College London.

Morris, M. [ed.] (1999) *Construction risk in river and estuary engineering.* Thomas Telford Ltd, London.

Sea levels

Pugh, D.T. (1987) *Tides, surges and mean sea-level.* Wiley.

Statistics – hydrology/engineering

Chatfield, C. (1983) *Statistics for technology.* 3rd edition. Chapman and Hall. (3rd edition reprinted with revisions, 1996, CRC Press.)

Clarke, R.T. (1994) *Statistical modelling in hydrology.* Wiley.

Helsel, D.R. and Hirsch, R.M. (1992) *Statistical methods in water resources.* Elsevier.

Holder, R.L. (1985) *Multiple regression in hydrology.* Institute of Hydrology.

Hosking, J.R.M. and Wallis, J.R. (1997) *Regional frequency analysis: an approach based on L-moments.* Cambridge University Press.

Metcalfe, A.V. (1994) *Statistics in engineering: a practical approach.* Chapman and Hall.

Metcalfe, A.V. (1997) *Statistics in civil engineering.* Arnold.

Urban drainage

Anon (1993) *Urban drainage – the natural way.* Hydro Research & Development Ltd., Clevedon.

Hall, M.J. (1984) *Urban hydrology.* Elsevier.

Index

5T rule 18

analogue catchment **6**, 13
    choosing 14
annual exceedance probability 67
annual maximum flood data 24
areal reduction factor 8
audit trails 55
automation of flood frequency calculations **9**, 58
avoiding joint probability problems 50, **86-87**

balanced resampling 69
    interval reversal when constructing confidence intervals by 73
balancing ponds 27-28, 45
baseflow, 19
basin-wide flood frequency estimates 48
BF 19
bibliography 95-101
boot-strapping 68

catchment boundaries, discrepancies in **9**, 13
catchment descriptors **8-10**, 60
catchment limits of FEH procedures 11
catchment models
    re-use of 35-36
catchment urbanisation
    allowance for 2, 21-23, **44-46**
    allowance for further expansion 45
    effect on catchment flood behaviour 27, **44-46**
    gross effect of 45
    judging extent of 44-45
    limit of method applicability 11-12, 21-23, 45-46
    net effect of 45
checklist of ideas, issues and resources 55
checklist when choosing method 23, **55**
choice of method of flood frequency estimation 17-23
    when catchment urbanised 21-23
    within rainfall-runoff approach 19
    within statistical approach 18-19
Chronology of British Hydrological Events 26, **90**
climate change 38-43
    baseline condition 41
    detection of 42-43
    scenarios 41
climate change impact assessment 40-42
    by modelling and use of scenarios 41
    spatial analogue method 41
    temporal analogue method 42
climate variability 12, 39, **42**, 90
combining gauged and historical flood data 92-94
confidence intervals 68-69
    resampling methods for deriving 71-73
confidence intervals by balanced resampling
    interval reversal when constructing 73

continuous simulation 46, **50**
contributing area 29

dam safety appraisal 20, 26, 31, 32, **51-54**
    need for conservatism in 53
damaging flood event 23
data transfers **6**, 17-18
    when donor catchment urbanised 22
design hydrograph 21
development
    flood runoff effects of 44-46, 61
development control 21-23, 27, **44-46**
dice problems 75-78
    how flooding problems differ from 77-78
    throw of two dice 75
    throw of two interdependent dice 76
digital catchment data 6-8, **9**
    to describe stream networks 58-60
digital terrain model 9
discrepancies in catchment boundaries **9**, 13
donor catchment **6**, 13
    choosing 14
double matrix method 75, **82-86**
    choosing the variables 82
    converting from continuous to discrete variables 82-83
    evaluating distribution of output values 84
    frequency adjustment factor 85
    inferring distribution of extreme output values 85
    setting up matrix of output values 84
    setting up matrix of probabilities 83
DTM 9
duration of rainfall
    sensitivity of scheme to **28-29**, 32
duty of care 9

exceptional storms 31-33
extreme events 31-35
extreme rainfall data 24

FARL 16
FEH CD-ROM 3, **8**, 14, 45, 46
flat catchments 9, 29
flood data CD-ROM 6, 8, **24**
flood defence
    freeboard allowance in 56
    hazard presented by 31
    over-design of 56
    responsibilities 1
    scheduling works 53
Flood Estimation Handbook
    aims 2
    only a guidebook **4**, 27
    structure 2-3
flood event analysis 53
    software for 9
flood event data 7, **25**
flood frequency calculations
    automation of **9**, 58

flood frequency curve **18**, 93
    that implies an upper bound 52
flood frequency estimation 1
    approaches to 5
    at confluence **74**, 81, 88
    choice of method 17-23
    continuous simulation approach to 46, **50**
    corner-cutting 37
    hybrid methods 18, **21**
    in tidally influenced river **74**, 81-88
    maxims for 5
flood peak data **24-25**, 33-35, 89-94
flood peak datasets
    revisions to FEH 25
floodplain 31, 47-48
    effect on flood frequency curve 93-94
    need for circumspection before siting balancing pond on 28
flood-poor periods 12, **43**, 90
flood rarity
    rainfall rarity does not determine 32
flood ratings 24, 36-37
flood-rich periods 12, **43**, 90
flood risk
    short-term forecasting of 53
flood risk assessment 1
flood risk mapping 47-50
    automated 49
    by design event method 49
    Environment Agency's 1999 map of Indicative Floodplain Extent 47-48
    IH Report 130 47
flood runoff effects of developments 44-46, 61
flood seasonality 12, 27, 48, 53
    assessing differences in 72-73
flood storage reservoir 28
Flood Studies Report 1
Flood Studies Supplementary Reports 1
floods
    sequences of 1, 36, 61
fluvial-tidal flood estimation 81-88
    structure function for 79-80
FORGEX method 15
frequency limits of FEH procedures 12
FSR rainfall-runoff method **5**, 9, 16, 17, 19-23, 57

gauging authorities 24, 25
Generalised Extreme Value distribution 16
Generalised Logistic distribution 16, 52, 93
geographical limits of FEH procedures 11
geomorphological evidence 26
global climate
    human influence on 38
global climate models 40-41
    downscaling problem 41
global warming
    implications for fluvial flooding 39-40
greenfield sites 46, 61
growth curve estimation 15, **18-19**

historical flood information 23, 25-26, 31-32, **89-94**
    interpretation of 91-94
    sources of 90
    use of 56
historical review
    augmenting flood estimates by 89-94
hybrid methods 18, **21**
hydraulic modelling 36-37, 48, 49, 79
hydrologically similar 6, **13-14**, 15

ICE Guide to Floods and Reservoir Safety 20, **51**
IHDTM 8
impounding reservoirs 51-54
incremental effect of urban development 11-12, 22-23, 27, **45-46**
index variable 15
interpretation of historical flood data 91-94
ITE land-cover map 44-45

jack-knifing 68
joint density function 76
joint probability problems 46, **74-88**
    assessing inter-variable dependence 84
    avoidance of 50, **86-87**
    choice of variables 77-79
    dependence 84
    double matrix method 75, **82-86**
    effect of dependence 76
    effective number of independent variables 88
    empirical density function 82
    erroneous multiplication of input-event rarities 77, 84
    event definition 81
    failure region 79-80
    frequency adjustment 84, 85
    historical emulation 87
    inferring distribution of extreme output values 85
    kernel density estimation 83
    matrix of output values 76, 84
    matrix of probabilities 76, 78, 83
    multivariate extreme method 88
    reservoir flood safety 88
    setting up 77-79
    structure function 75, **79-80**, 87
    system model 79
    time-blocking 79, 82

karstic catchments 13, 35

land-cover map 44-45
landslides 31
land-use changes
    impact on flood frequency 29-30, 44-46, 61
Langbein's formula 67
local data 6
Logistic distribution 52

marginal density function 76
    evaluation from cumulative distribution 83
matrix method *see under* double matrix method

Micro-FSR 9
miscellaneous floppy disk 9
mistakes 10, 27-37

newspaper records 26, 90
non-stationarity **42-43**, 60, 69-71
null hypothesis 69-70

outliers 33-34
     missing 34

palæoflood data 26
paper maps 13
peaks-over-threshold flood data 15, **24**
permeable catchments 13, 20
permutation testing
     checking for trend by 69-71, 73
phasing of runoff 27
planning applications 27, 30-31
pooling-group 15, 19
probable maximum flood 12, 20, 26, **51**, 52
probable maximum precipitation 12, **51**
PROPWET 16
public perception of flood risk 32
     uncertainty in 61
public safety
     flood frequency estimation for 51-54
     special precautions at sensitive sites 53

QBAR 15, 71
QMED 15, 18, 71
     recommended method for estimating 18

rainfall data 24, 90
rainfall depth-duration frequency
     procedure for 8, 12, 24
rainfall frequency estimation **15**, 17
rainfall-runoff approach 5, 16, 19-23
rating equations 24, 36
recommended methods 17-23
     growth curve estimation 18-19
     parameter estimation in rainfall-runoff method 19
     QMED estimation 18
reconciling estimates 21
recurrence interval 67
red-lining 47
references 63-66, 95-101
related technical guidance
     bibliography of 95-101
reporting of studies 36, 49, **55**
resampling methods 68-73
     balanced resampling **69**, 71-73
     for exploring uncertainty 68
     sampling with replacement 69
reservoir flood estimation 20, **51-54**, 57
     joint probability problems in 53, 88
     new approaches to 53-54
reservoir flood routing, software for 9

reservoir flood safety
    ICE guide to 2, 20, 51-52
    recommended use of rainfall-runoff method in 20, 51-53
reservoir lag effect 28
reservoir storage
    attenuating effect of 21, 28
return period 1, 13, **67**, 89
    on annual maximum scale 67
    on peaks-over-threshold scale 67
revision policy 7, **10**
risk 1, 13, **67**
risk equation 13, **67**, 89
RMED 15

sampling error 68
seasonal effects 12, 27, 48, 53, 72
short-term flood risk 53
small catchments 9, **11**, 14, 22
software limitations 9, 35
software packages 3, **8**
soil moisture deficit **12**, 16
spatially extensive extremes **31-32**, 34
SPR 19
standard percentage runoff 19
statistical analysis of peak flows 5
statistical flood frequency estimation procedure 9, 18-23
    robust against outliers 33-34
    urban adjustments 22, 45
step change **42**, 70-71
storm-sewer design 2, 57
structure function 75, **79-80**, 87
subject site 5
    inclusion in pooling-group 19
subject-site locator 8

target return period 18
technical guidance 95-101
time of concentration 29
Tp 19
trend detection **42-43**, 60-61, 69-71, 73
two-component analysis of extremes 34
T-year flood 67

UK flood series
    trends in 43, **60**
UK river flooding
    patterns in 12
uncertainty
    of flood frequency estimates 17, 21, **56**
    resampling methods for exploring 68, 71-72
unit hydrograph derivation
    software for 9
unit hydrograph/losses model 19, 22
unit hydrograph time-to-peak 19
urban drainage
    soakaways 46
    source-control methods 45-46, 61
urbanisation *see under* catchment urbanisation

URBEXT 12, 16, 21, **44**

water-year 24
whole catchment modelling **50**, 61
WINFAP-FEH 3, 7, **9**
    extending flood data held in 24